Fraction Fun

Through Cooperative Learning

Laurie Kagan
In consultation with Dr. Spencer Kagan

Kagan

Kagan Publishing
981 Calle Amanecer
San Clemente, CA 92673
1(800) 933-2667
www.KaganOnline.com

ISBN: 978-1-879097-15-5

Table of Contents

Team Structures

Explorations

Classbuilding Structures

Lessons

Naming Fractions

Comparing Fractions

Equivalent Fractions

Addition of Fractions

Subtraction of Fractions

Multiplication of Fractions

Division of Fractions

Where to Find the Structures

Foreword

by Dr. Spencer Kagan

The publication of this book completes a circle. When I was first developing the structural approach to cooperative learning, I took pride in telling teachers that cooperative learning structures are content free — they are tools which can be used to deliver any curriculum. For a number of years, I emphasized that learning structures was a better way for teachers to learn cooperative learning, because the structures can be used at any grade-level and with any content. I pointed out how they could visit certain schools in which there was almost no cooperative learning, even though a few years before almost every teacher had been successfully implementing an extensive cooperative learning program. What had happened? The cooperative learning they had been doing was part of a curriculum package, and when the curriculum was changed, out went the cooperative learning. I pointed out that when teachers train in the structural approach, even when their curriculum shifts, or their grade level changes, they still implement cooperative learning. Once a teacher knows a cooperative learning structure well, she/he will never abandon it. You don't abandon useful tools just because you are doing a different job: When carpenters move from one construction site to another, do you see them throw away their saws or hammers?

What does all this have to do with teaching fractions? I'm getting to that. Just bear with me a bit longer.

After a number of years of training teachers in the pure structural approach to cooperative learning, I got a rude awakening. I had focused exclusively on the *how* of teaching, leaving the *what* of teaching, the content, up to each teacher. The rude awakening came when I started visiting classrooms of teachers after they had mastered a number of structures and were implementing cooperative learning with their own curriculum. Yes, it was true: they reported, and I observed, that they were more efficiently covering their curriculum because they knew a range of cooperative learning structures. And yes, it was also true that they were enjoying teaching more and their students were enjoying learning more. But there was a problem. In some classes the teachers were efficiently covering a curriculum which never should have been delivered!

Thus this book.

It was because of the prodding of Laurie Kagan that I began examining curriculum. I began to study the latest in Mathematics instruction, and Whole Language instruction, and discovered that the cooperative learning structures we were developing were far more powerful than we had imagined. For example, as we teach for understanding in mathematics, different cooperative learning structures can be used for more efficient teaching at different stages of the instructional process. We found a natural marriage. Today, we would no more think of implementing the new Mathematics standards without cooperative learning structures, than we would think of building a house without using saws and hammers.

To share the power of this marriage of structures with curriculum, I asked Laurie Kagan to write this book. Laurie is the best trainer in the structural approach I have seen. For years she was both the Director of Elementary Education for the State of Nevada and was in charge of implementing the National Mathematics Standards for the state. She knows both the cooperative learning structures and the best of mathematics instruction inside out. What she has done in creating this book is to pick the best structure/content combinations for Explorations, Classbuilding, and Concept Development at each stage of learning fractions. This book presents a complete curriculum in fractions, delivered through cooperative learning structures.

Thus we have come full circle. Whereas I once prided myself in not teaching content, leaving content up to the teachers, I now take pride that we can offer a complete instructional package — the best of cooperative learning structures coupled with the best of mathematics curriculum.

This book was initially circulated in draft form, and met tremendous success. Teachers across the United States and Canada have been reporting that through the lessons in the book, even their advanced students, are for the first time discovering the meaning behind the rote algorithms they had been using. Through the lessons students move from a focus on getting answers to a focus on exploring mathematical relations.

I am confident you will find this book a welcome addition to your storehouse of teaching tools — whether you are introducing fractions for the first time, or whether you are working with students who know well how to get answers, but who need to explore the meaning behind the operations they are executing. This book is a tool to be used as we carry out an overdue revolution — a revolution empowering students to work together, explore their world, and construct understanding based on their own experience.

Spencer Kagan
April, 1993

Acknowledgments

Many thanks go to so many people who have given me ideas both directly and indirectly. They challenged me to seek out new learning and opened my eyes to outdated teaching methods and tiresome predictable course work. I learned that mathematics can be fun as I adapted a fresh perspective on concepts and how I present them to students.

I owe a great deal to Jackie Berrum who traveled with me as we trained thousands of teachers. She gave me the chance to bounce off new ideas and was always there with support and feedback.

To Sally Scott, I give thanks for opening my eyes to what great teaching really is. We decided to grow and learn together by attending numerous workshops — to explore how to teach mathematics.

Catherine Hurlbert and Benjamin Taylor put in countless hours revising each draft. They managed with efficiency all the corrections necessary to enable this final text to be produced. Celso Rodriguez created the delightful art and page layout.

Also — this book would not be possible without Spencer Kagan. He stood by me, encouraging me to stay with producing this workbook. His professional insight, challenging ideas, editing skills, and constant support made this book possible. He knows I enjoy teaching and creating new content much more than writing my ideas down on paper. Without him, it's simple — there would be no book!

Laurie Kagan

Laurie Kagan
April, 1993

Introduction

The traditional method for teaching division of fractions is to say to students, "Yours is not to question why, just invert and multiply." Giving students rules to follow may let them get answers, but does not help them understand math concepts. In the long run teaching without understanding disempowers students. This book is designed to provide an alternative: To empower students by teaching for understanding, creating a love of math.

This book is based on the premise that an understanding and love of math comes through a discovery process based on plenty of hands-on experience with manipulatives in a supportive context. The book follows closely the standards provided by the National Council of Teachers of Mathematics, allowing students to obtain each new concept by working sequentially through the concrete, connecting and symbolic levels.

Free Explorations

To provide the initial positive experience with fractions, I strongly recommend students first freely explore fraction manipulatives with little structure. Children need a chance to explore, discover, arrange, build, and play before they are ready for direct instruction. This takes place through Free Explorations: You simply pass out the manipulatives, let the students play with them, and then ask them what they have learned and what they are discovering.

Guided Explorations

Following the period of Free Explorations we move into Guided Discovery. In Guided Discovery there is still little instruction, but children learn what fractions are and the relationships among them as they work together to explore specific problems. The book provides 14 Guided Explorations to get you started. For example, in one of the Explorations, students simply work to "name halves." They choose a fraction piece and then work together to discover if there are two identical pieces which can build the target piece. In another Exploration students simply try to find the longest piece they can build with four fraction pieces.

Classbuilding Structures

After Explorations, we move into Classbuilding. The approach here is to use cooperative learning structures to create fun activities in which children learn more about fractions while working together as a class. For example, in one Line-Up activity each child selects his/her own fraction and then all the students in the class line up by the size of their fraction, from smallest to largest. In Similarity Groups, children find everyone in the class who has selected the same fraction as themselves. In the Classbuilding section, you will find five cooperative learning structures. Each structure has many activities to get you started. Through classbuilding we create a love for and familiarity with fractions, in a fun, supportive context. Feel free to add you own activities and watch your class come alive helping each other learn about fractions.

Cooperative Learning Lessons

The book shows how to teach all of the most important fraction concepts through cooperative learning activities. There are twenty-four lessons. Students start at the beginning, learning to identify fractions. Each lesson is designed to be taught cooperatively in teams of four. Students use hands-on manipulatives including fraction dice and spinners to make learning fractions fun and easy. The lessons are designed for students from grades 2 to 12. Even students who can divide fractions with ease using traditional methods can benefit by going through the levels of these lessons — to create the understanding which should underlie the symbolic abilities.

The lessons are paced, and students need to master each lesson before moving to the next. The concepts taught through the lessons are:

- Exploring Fractions
- Addition of Fractions
- Naming Fractions
- Multiplication of Fractions
- Comparing Fractions
- Subtraction of Fractions
- Equivalent Fractions
- Division of Fractions

To teach for understanding, each concept must be taught at three different levels, with practice provided at each. Instruction of each new concept must start with the *concrete* level — students build with manipulatives as they solve each problem. Next, we teach at the *connecting* level — students learn to draw a picture of each problem and add the numbers or symbols. In the last level, the *symbolic* level, students work out problems with numbers. Using all three levels, students learn what mathematics is, not just how to get answers. If they forget a rule they will be able to reason through the process.

My Hope

Fractions are one of the hardest concepts for us to teach and for students to understand. The old methods of having students memorize rules don't work. Cooperative learning, too, can be difficult. But it can provide a wonderfully supportive, fun atmosphere within which to learn. In the book, I have tried to provide simple-to-follow lesson plans to teach the most fundamental fraction concepts. Through the lessons, students have the opportunity to interpret mathematical theories and construct mathematical understanding for themselves. My hope is that by providing step-by-step ideas this book will make teaching fractions through cooperative learning easy for you, and exciting for your students. By walking with your students step-by-step through these explorations, classbuilding activities, and lessons you will provide your pupils with a life long set of skills and a love for math.

Definitions

Fraction: A term consisting of a numerator and a denominator, indicating some number of equal parts of a whole.

Denominator: The term below the line in a fraction, indicating the number of equal parts each whole is divided into.

Numerator: The term above the line in a fraction, indicating some number of the equal parts.

Restatement: If we divide one whole into equal parts, the denominator tells how many parts there are. The numerator indicates how many of these equal parts we select.

Examples: Given the fraction 2/6, 2 is the numerator and 6 is the denominator. The fraction 2/6 indicates we have broken a whole into six equal parts and selected two. The fraction 6/2, indicates we have broken a number of wholes into two parts each, and have selected six of those parts.

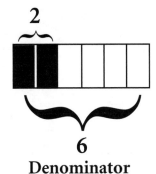

Numerator $=$ $\dfrac{2}{6}$
Denominator $=$

Lowest Common Denominator: The lowest number into which two denominators will evenly divide.

Role Card: A card indicating the special job of a student.

/ *Checker* △   / *Praiser* △

Making The Manipulatives

Fraction Sheet
8½ x 11 colored card stock

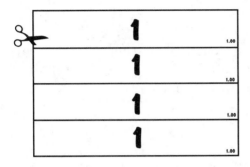

Making Fraction Bars and Pieces

Each team of four receives a set of 10 different colored fraction sheets. The Fraction Bar Kit© by Kagan and Robertson provides all the necessary fraction pieces for 36 students. The teammates cut each of the 10 sheets along the lines into four fraction bars. Each student gets 1 fraction bar of each color. Next, each student cuts apart each of his or her bars, along the black lines, into the correct number of pieces. They end up with one 1, two ½'s, three ⅓'s, and so on. When they have finished cutting out all of the pieces, they store the pieces in an envelope or baggie.

Step 1: There are 4 bars per fraction sheet. Have each team cut the fraction sheet into four bars, so each student gets one bar.

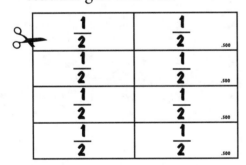

Step 2: Each students receives 1 fraction bar, and cuts it into the correct sizes.

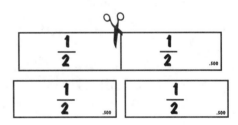

Step 3: Have students store all their fraction pieces in baggies or envelopes.

Color-Key for the Fraction Bars in the Cooperative Learning Fraction Kit:

1 = Light Red $\frac{1}{4}$ = Yellow $\frac{1}{8}$ = Dark Red $\frac{1}{12}$ = Mustard Yellow

$\frac{1}{2}$ = Green $\frac{1}{5}$ = Orange $\frac{1}{10}$ = Teal Green $\frac{1}{16}$ = Fuschia

$\frac{1}{3}$ = Pink $\frac{1}{6}$ =Light Green

Fraction Bars

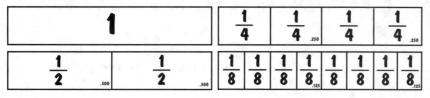

Each student gets one fraction bar of each size fraction. The kit contains 10 different sized fractions.

Fraction Pieces

Each student cuts each of his/her fraction bars on the lines to create fraction pieces: Two halves, three thirds, four fourths, etc.

Concrete and Symbolic Dice

Each team receives a sheet with one concrete die, and another sheet with a symbolic die. They cut out the dice along the lines and then fold them into cubes.

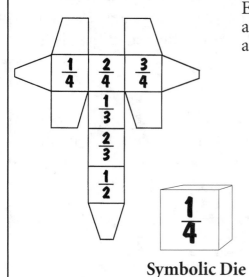

Symbolic Die
(Assembled)

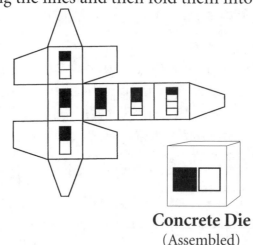

Concrete Die
(Assembled)

Fraction Spinners   Each team cuts out 2 spinners and connects them with a brad.

Team Structures

Numbered Heads Together

See Explorations 5, 10, 11

Numbered Heads Together is a simple structure, consisting of four steps: (1) Students Number Off; (2) Teacher Announces a Question; (3) Students Put their Heads Together; and (4) Teacher Calls a Number.

Step 1. Students Number Off. Each student on the team has a different number.

Step 2. Teacher Asks a Question. The question asked of students during Step 2 is formulated as a directive. Instead of saying, "What fraction of the pie has been eaten?" the teacher says, "Make sure everyone on the team can explain what fraction of the pie has been eaten."

The question may be either high or low consensus, but is phrased accordingly. For example, for a high consensus question, the teacher might say, "Put your heads together and name how many pizzas it will take to feed nine people if we divide each pizza into six pieces." For a higher level thinking question, the teacher might say, "Make sure you are all ready to predict how many wholes we can build from the 37 fraction pieces in this baggie."

Variation:

To quicken the pace, the teacher may sometimes provide a time frame for students. So, for example, the teacher might say, "How many pieces are in one third; you have thirty seconds to make sure everyone on your team knows."

Step 3. Heads Together. Students literally put their heads together and make sure everyone knows the answer. The role of the Checker may be added here.

Step 4. Teacher Calls a Number. The teacher will call a number at random and students with that number raise their hands to be called upon if they know the answer, as in the traditional classroom.

Variation:

A Numbered Heads Together spinner or Student Selector for the overhead is available, and makes the structure more game-like. The spinner is also handy because teachers do not have to remember which numbers they have called.

If the answer is within the capacity of most teams, but only one or two students raise their hands, the the teacher might say, "Not enough Number Twos have their hands up; I'll give you one more minute, make sure all your Number Twos know the answer."

If the question has several answers, such as, "Name six fractions equivalent to one half," the teacher will get fuller participation by asking for the number ones to name one equivalent fraction, the number twos to name another, and so on.

If a student gives a partially correct response, the teacher might ask, "Is there a Number Three who can add to that response?"

1. Students Number Off

2. Teacher Presents Problem

3. Heads Together

4. A Number is Called

Laurie Kagan: *Fraction Fun*

Kagan Publishing • 1 (800) 933-2667 • www.KaganOnline.com

Pairs Check

See Lessons 9, 12, 15, 18, 20, 21

1. "A" does problem

2. "B" checks

3. "B" praises

4. "B" does problem

Steps of Pairs Check

Sitting in teams of 4, each person has a partner on the same side of the table. One is "A", the other one is "B." Each A, B pair share one worksheet.

Step 1. "A" does the problem. In each pair, "A" works on the problem while "B", the coach, watches, and helps, if necessary.

Step 2. "B" Checks. The coach checks partner's work for agreement.

Step 3. "B" Praises. If the partners agree on the answer, the coach (B) praises his or her partner.

Steps 4-6. Partners Switch Roles. The partners switch roles and repeat steps 1-3. The student who had been the coach (B) now becomes the problem solver, while the other student (A) becomes the coach.

Step 7. Pairs Check. Each Pair compares its answers with the pair on the other side of the table. If they disagree and are unable to figure why, four hands go up, a signal to the teacher that the team needs help.

Step 8. Team Celebrates. If the team agrees on the answer, they celebrate with a team hand shake or cheer.

Teams will finish at different rates, so an attractive content-related sponge activity built into the worksheet is usually a good idea.

To help students do Pairs Check, a Pairs Check Worksheet like the one on the next following page is often used.

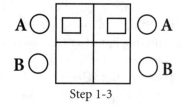
Step 1-3

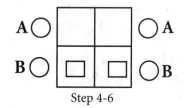
Step 4-6

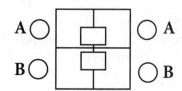
Step 7: papers go side by side to check

5. "A" checks

6. "A" praises

7. Pairs Check

8. Team Celebrates

Laurie Kagan: *Fraction Fun*
Kagan Publishing • 1 (800) 933-2667 • www.KaganOnline.com

Pairs ✓

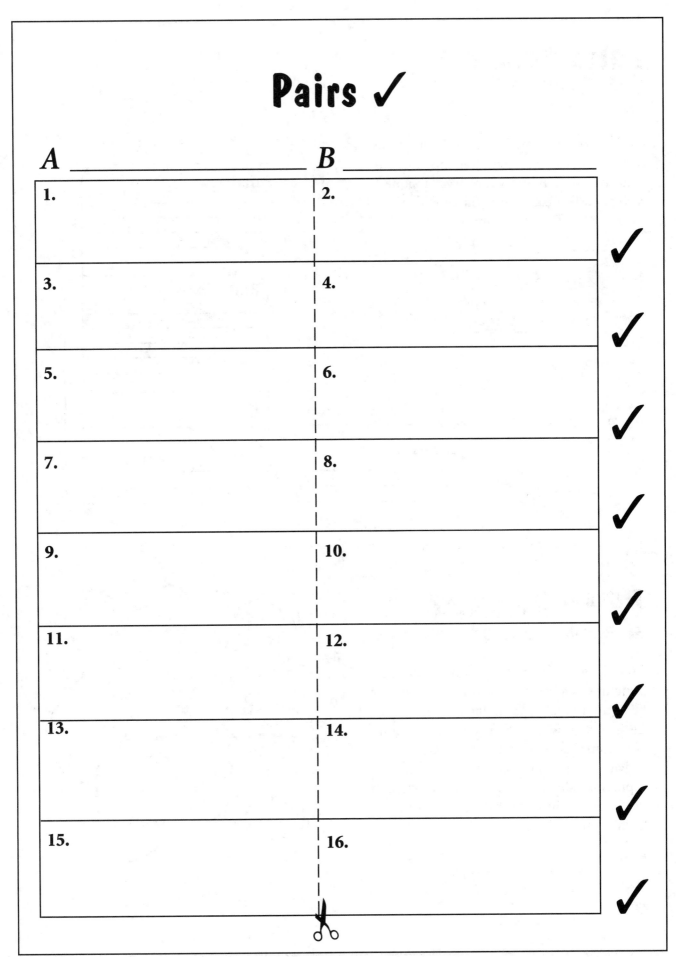

A _____   B _____

1.	**2.**	✓
3.	**4.**	✓
5.	**6.**	✓
7.	**8.**	✓
9.	**10.**	✓
11.	**12.**	✓
13.	**14.**	✓
15.	**16.**	✓

Pairs Compare

See Exploration 8
See Lesson 3

Often following a Pair Discussion, pairs discuss
with another pair which ideas they came up
with in common and which were unique to
each pair. This can be formalized with a Venn
Diagram for the group to record ideas.

Pair 1
_____
_____
_____
_____

Both
_____
_____
_____
_____
_____

Pair 2
_____
_____
_____
_____

Neither
_____
_____
_____
_____
_____

Pair Discussion

See Explorations 7, 13

The simplest of all cooperative learning
structures is a Pair Discussion. Students may
be in traditional rows, on the rug, at a learning center, or within their cooperative teams.
You simply say, "With a partner, talk over..."
A Pair Discussion over any low consensus
topic is usually better than a team discussion
because it produces twice the amount of active
participation.

Pairs discuss

RoundRobin

See Exploration 1, 14

In RoundRobin, all responses are verbal.

Step 1. Teacher asks a question or poses a problem with many possible answers.

Step 2. Students answer orally, each in turn.

Teacher presents problem.

Students respond orally, each in turn.

RallyRobin

See Exploration 2
See Exploration 13

This is a variation of RoundRobin that increases the simultaneity because students are working in pairs.

Step 1. Teacher asks a question, poses a problem, or gives directions for discussion.

Step 2. In pairs, students take turns giving answers or ideas.

Teacher presents problem.

Students take turns responding orally.

RoundTable
See Lessons 4, 5, 6

Step 1. Teacher asks a question or poses a problem with many possible answers.

Step 2. Students answer in writing, each in turn by passing a single sheet of paper and a single pencil around the table to record answers.

Content Variations: Students answer in turn by passing a single sheet of paper and a single pencil around the table to record answers.

Teacher presents problem.

Note: Use a spinner or draw a number so the same student does not start each time.

Each student responds in turn.

Variation:

RoundTable with Rotating Roles
See Lessons 7, 8

Each teammember receives a different role. As the students take turns, each one carries out his/her role assignment. When they are finished with problem 1, all role cards are passed 1 person clockwise and play continues.

RallyTable

See Explorations 3, 6, 9, 12
See Lessons 1, 2, 3, 11, 13, 14, 17, 22

This structure is a variation of RoundTable, but students work in pairs (2 papers, 2 pencils).

Step 1. Teacher asks a question, poses a problem, or gives directions for a worksheet.

Step 2. In pairs, students answer by writing one answer and passing the paper back and forth. One student works the problem while the other student watches, helps, coaches and praises.

Teacher presents problem.

Students take turns responding.

Simultaneous RoundTable

See Lessons 24

This structure is yet another variation of RoundTable. Simultaneity is increased because students are writing at the same time, then passing (4 papers, 4 pencils).

Step 1. This step is the same as in RallyTable. Teacher asks a question, poses a problem, or gives directions for a worksheet.

Step 2. All students respond on a sheet of paper. They then pass it clockwise, check the previous problem, and do the next problem.

1. Teacher presents problem.

2. Students respond on sheet of paper.

2. Students pass paper clockwise & check problem.

Team Discussion

See Exploration 1, 14

A Team Discussion, just like a Pair Discussion, is an unstructured discussion within a group. The only difference is that in a Pair Discussion, the group size is two, whereas in a Team Discussion, the group size usually is four.

Step 1: Teacher assigns a topic to be discussed within a group.

Step 2: Students within their teams talk it over.

Step 3: Students share their ideas.

1. Teacher assigns topic

2. Team Discussion

3. Students share ideas

Laurie Kagan: *Fraction Fun*

Kagan Publishing • 1 (800) 933-2667 • www.KaganOnline.com

Think-Pair-Share

See Lesson 19

1. Problem Posed

Step 1: The teacher poses a problem.

Step 2: Students think alone about the question for a specified amount of time.

Step 3: Students form pairs to discuss the question with someone in the class, usually a teammate.

Step 4: Students are called upon to share the answer with the class. Students are held accountable for listening to their partner because during share time, sometimes they are called upon to share the answer they heard from their partner.

2. Think Time

Variation:

A. Think-Pair-Square

See Lesson 16, 23

This structure is the same as Think-Pair-Share except in Step 4. In step 4, the pairs share their answers with their teammates.

4. Square with Team

3. Pair Work

B. Think-Build-Pair-Share

See Exploration 4

This structure is the same as Think-Pair-Share except after each student thinks, they individually build the answer with manipulatives.

4. Share with Class

C. Think-Build-Pair-Square

See Lesson 10

This structure is the same as Think-Build-Pair-Share except that instead of sharing their answers within the class, they discuss their answers with their teammates.

Laurie Kagan: *Fraction Fun*

Kagan Publishing • 1 (800) 933-2667 • www.KaganOnline.com

Explorations

It is important to remember that whenever a new manipulative is introduced in a classroom, students need lots of time to explore the manipulatives before being asked to use them in a particular lesson. It is difficult, even impossible, to focus students' attention through direct instruction on a mathematics concept, if students are intrigued and curious about the manipulatives. By allowing them to follow their interest in the manipulatives, as they play with the concrete manipulatives, mathematical ideas and concepts will be discovered.

Rock-Paper-Fractions

▶ **Goal:** The goal is to try to "out think" teammembers by selecting the largest fraction piece each time.

▶ **Structure:** RoundRobin
Team Discussion

Step

1 In teams of 4, each student puts **on their lap** the following pieces:
2 1/2's
2 1/3's
2 1/4's
1 1/6

Step

2 Students select the fraction of their choice and put it in their **left hand**, hiding it under their desk.

Step

4 First, students name orally the fraction they selected using RoundRobin, then discuss and compare all 4 fractions that are showing to find the largest.

If one student has the largest fraction, the other three clap for that student. If two or more tie for largest, the remaining students clap for them.

They then place the fraction they just used on top of their desk in a pile and...

... continue until all fractions are used.

Step

3 Students place their **right hand on their desk** in a fist and together as a class they touch their desk in unison and say "1", "2" and on "3", each student pulls out the fraction piece they selected to show on "3."

▶ **Challenge:** Let students select different fractions to start with.

Laurie Kagan: *Fraction Fun*
Kagan Publishing • 1 (800) 933-2667 • www.KaganOnline.com

Serving Pizza

▶ **Goal:** The goal is to figure out the equivalent mixed number.

▶ **Structure: RallyTable**

In pairs, divide each circle into eighths. Ask students to imagine that the circles are pizzas. Students take turns figuring out how many pizzas and fractional parts of pizzas would be needed to serve each person one slice. Answers are to be written as mixed numbers at the bottom of the page.

Answers

1. 9 people? $(1\frac{1}{8}$ pizzas)

2. 17 people? $(2\frac{1}{8}$ pizzas)

3. 23 people? $(2\frac{7}{8}$ pizzas)

4. 7 people? $(\frac{7}{8}$ pizza)

5. 15 people? $(1\frac{7}{8}$ pizzas)

6. 11 people? $(1\frac{3}{8}$ pizzas)

7. 13 people? $(1\frac{5}{8}$ pizzas)

8. 21 people? $(2\frac{5}{8}$ pizzas)

9. 16 people?   (2 pizzas)

10. 5 people? $(\frac{1}{8}$ pizza)

11. 19 people? $(2\frac{3}{8}$ pizzas)

12. 24 people?   (3 pizzas)

▶ **Challenge:**
Let students change the number of slices in the pizzas and use the same questions.
The pizzas are divided into 4ths.
The pizzas are divided into 6ths.

Serving Pizza

WORKSHEET

Answers

1. _____ 2. _____ 3. _____ 4. _____ 5. _____ 6. _____

7. _____ 8. _____ 9. _____ 10. _____ 11. _____ 12. _____

Laurie Kagan: *Fraction Fun*

Kagan Publishing • 1 (800) 933-2667 • www.KaganOnline.com

Naming Halves

 Goal: The goal is to find all possible halves.

 Structure: RallyTable

In pairs, students take turns discovering all the color combinations rules of 1/2.

Step

Find a rule. **Example:** Blue is 1/2 of red.

Step

Draw your rule.

Red	
Blue	Blue

Step

Write the statement "B=1/2 R". Continue exploring and building all the other halves you can find taking turns, record the statement for each half you find.

 Challenge: Continue with 3rds, 4ths, 6ths. What rules can you find?

Unique Patterns

▶ **Goal:** Have students discover equivalent fractions on a multiplication chart.

▶ **Structure:** Think-Build-Pair-Share

Step

1 Think. Have students look at a multiplication table and see if they can find the pattern for equivalent fractions. Draw for them the sample below of 1/2. Show them how the pattern works.

Step

2 Build. Individually, have students fill in the blank multiplication chart. Then Ask the students to search for a pattern that shows equivalent fractions. Circle each pattern they find with a different color crayon.

Step

3 Pair. Ask students to pair with their partner and share the pattern they found.

Step

4 Square. All 4 worksheets are placed side by side and the team discusses what they discovered and looks for any new patterns.

Sample:

Equivalent Fractions Chart

X	1	2	3	4	5	6	7	8	9	10
1	1	2	3	4	5	6	7	8	9	10
2	2	4	6	8	10	12	14	16	18	20
3	3	6	9	12	15	18	21	24	27	30
4	4	8	12	16	20	24	28	32	36	40

Explanation: 1/2 = 2/4 = 3/6 = 4/8 ...

Laurie Kagan: *Fraction Fun*
Kagan Publishing • 1 (800) 933-2667 • www.KaganOnline.com

Unique Patterns

WORKSHEET

Equivalent Fraction Chart

X	1	2	3	4	5	6	7	8	9	10
1										
2										
3										
4										
5										
6										
7										
8										
9										
10										

Chart Puzzles

Exploration 5

▶ **Goal:** To find the value of all the other colors of bars when a different color is assigned the value of "One" each time.

▶ **Structure:** Numbered Heads Together

Start with the ___light red___, ___green___, ___pink___, and ___yellow___ fraction pieces turned over so only the back sides are showing.

Sample: If light red has the value of 1, then green would be worth 1/2, pink would be worth 1/3, and yellow would be worth 1/4. Have students in teams of 4 finish the matrix box and make sure everyone on their team can explain why they placed the fraction numbers in each square.

Finish the Chart

light red	1			
green	$\frac{1}{2}$	1		
pink	$\frac{1}{3}$		1	
yellow	$\frac{1}{4}$			1

▶ **Challenge:** Make another chart with different colors.

Chart Puzzles

WORKSHEET

Puzzle 1

Color

Light Red	**1**			
Green				
Pink				
Yellow				

Puzzle 2

Color

Mixed-Up Rainbows

▶ **Goal:** The goal is to find all the possible ways to build 1.

▶ **Structure: RallyTable**

All fraction bars are turned over so that no numbers are showing.

Using 1 as **your base workboard**, Partners Find all the combo's you can build to make 1.

Draw and label all the possiblities you discovered.

1/2 green, 1/2 yellow

Sample	green	yellow	yellow

$$G + Y + Y = 1$$

Laurie Kagan: *Fraction Fun*
Kagan Publishing • 1 (800) 933-2667 • www.KaganOnline.com

Rainbow Puzzles

▶ **Goal:** To solve each puzzle with fraction bars.

▶ **Structure: Pair Discussion**

Sample: Make the total length of the bar always equal to 1.
Puzzle: 1/3 yellow, 2/3 dark red

Answer

yellow	yellow	dark red	dark red	dark red	dark red
y	+	y	+	dr	+	dr	+	dr	+	dr

Puzzle

1
1/2 green, 1/4 yellow, 1/4 dark red

2
1/2 green, 1/2 yellow

3
3/10 teal green, 1/2 green, 1/5 orange

4
1/3 pink, 1/3 lt. green, 1/3 mustard yellow

5
1/3 light green, 2/6 pink

6
1 green

7
1/2 yellow, 3/8 dark red, 1/8 fuschia

Building Rectangles

▶ **Goal:** The goal is to find the missing pieces.

▶ **Structure: Pairs Compare**

Step 1
Build the rectangles below with fraction pieces on your desk.

Step 2
Finish building the rectangles using only the number of pieces asked for.

Step 3
Label your results. Pairs compare after each rectangle is built.

Rectangle 1   Use only 6 pieces

$\frac{1}{4}$ yellow		
		$\frac{1}{2}$ green

Rectangle 2   Use only 6 pieces

	$\frac{1}{3}$ pink	
$\frac{1}{6}$ lt green		

▶ **Challenge 1:**
Can you design a new puzzle for your partner?

▶ **Challenge 2:**
What would these look like if each piece was reduced by half?
How many pieces would each puzzle have?
Can you draw the results?

Lengths

▶ **Goal:** The goal is to find all the possible lengths you can build using only two colors.

▶ **Structure: RallyTable**

Using only two colors and no color more than two times, how many different lengths can you build? Record your results with colors and fractions drawn.

Sample 1: Red and Pink

| $\frac{1}{2}$ | $\frac{1}{2}$ | $\frac{1}{3}$ | $\frac{1}{3}$ |

Sample 2: Red and Yellow

| $\frac{1}{2}$ | $\frac{1}{2}$ | $\frac{1}{4}$ | $\frac{1}{4}$ |

Sample Recording Sheet:

	Fractions				Colors
1.	$\frac{1}{2}$	$\frac{1}{2}$	$\frac{1}{3}$	$\frac{1}{3}$	Red and Pink
2.	$\frac{1}{2}$	$\frac{1}{2}$	$\frac{1}{4}$	$\frac{1}{4}$	Red and Yellow

Longest

▶ **Goal:** To discover what pieces are used to build long fraction bars.

▶ **Structure:** Numbered Heads Together

What is the longest piece you can build using only four fraction pieces?
1. Using any combination of pieces?
2. Using each size piece once only?

Draw Your Results

Laurie Kagan: *Fraction Fun*
Kagan Publishing • 1 (800) 933-2667 • www.KaganOnline.com

Smallest

▶ **Goal:** To discover what pieces are used to build short fraction pieces.

▶ **Structure:** Numbered Heads Together

What is the smallest piece you can build using only 4 fraction pieces?
1. Using any combination of pieces?
2. Using each size piece once only?

Draw Your Results

Smaller

Goal: To discover how different size fraction pieces compare in size.

Structure: RallyTable

How many ways can you lay down 4 pieces so that each one is smaller than the one on its left?

Start with:

$\frac{1}{2}$	$\frac{1}{3}$	$\frac{1}{4}$	$\frac{1}{5}$

Step 1

"A" begins by building the sample shown and "B" draws with crayons the diagram to record the fraction strip that is built.

Step 2

"B" builds a fraction strip trying to make it just a bit smaller than the last one.

Step 3

"A" draws the diagram to record the results.

* Keep making smaller fraction strips, using only 4 pieces each time.
* Each time, be sure to trade builders and recorders and record your results.
* You may reuse your fraction bars as needed.

Challenge: Use 5 pieces, and make as many lengths as you can.

Steps

▶ **Goal:** To discover all fractions that are half of another.

▶ **Structure: Pair Discussion**

Step

1 Set out one fraction piece of each size.

Step

2 Place the 1 whole fraction at the bottom to use as a base.

Step

3 Try to decrease each fraction piece by half its size each time.

Sample:

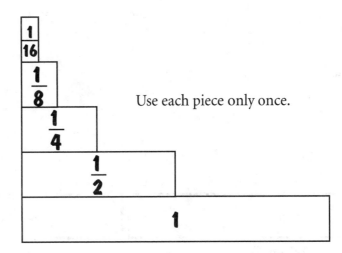

Use each piece only once.

Using the worksheet on the following page, what other halves can your students discover?

Steps

How many steps will you need to build?

1

Step 1

1

Step 2

1

Step 3

1

Step 4

Exploration 14

Fraction Word Riddles

▶ **Goal:** The concept of fraction parts of a whole can be demonstrated using word riddles.

▶ **Structure:** RoundRobin
Team Discussion

Step
1 Write the questions on 3X5 cards and each answer on the back.

Step
2 Begin with the word "BILL." Have students note that it contains four letters or four parts. Each letter, then, is one of four letters or 1/4 of the word. In each riddle the fraction given is the clue to the number of letters in the answer. **Sample:** What 3/4 of **BILL** could mean you are sick? (ILL)

Step
3 Have students pass out the cards like a deck of cards.

Step
4 Have students rotate reading each question to their teammates. The team discusses the answer and checks the back of the cards to see if they are correct.

1. What 3/8 of **FRACTION** do you need to perform? (ACT)

2. What 4/6 of **RIDDLE** do you do on a bike? (RIDE)

3. What 3/8 of **ESTIMATE** means you could have eaten? (ATE)

4. What 3/7 of **CONTAIN** do you do at the beach? (TAN)

5. What animal is 1/4 **COLA** and 2/3 of **MAT**? (CAT)

6. What 4/7 of **DISPLAY** is what you do at recess? (PLAY)

▶ Challenge students to create their own!

Laurie Kagan: *Fraction Fun*
Kagan Publishing • 1 (800) 933-2667 • www.KaganOnline.com

Laurie Kagan: *Fraction Fun*
Kagan Publishing • 1 (800) 933-2667 • www.KaganOnline.com

Classbuilding Structures

Classbuilding is a way of creating a positive climate in the whole class. Students get to know each other and experience each other's support while practicing mathematics.

Formations

Students form figures with their bodies by holding hands or standing near each other. Sometimes they are not allowed to talk.

Make: **Answer**

1. The number 1   1

2. Long rectangle

3. Divide it into 2 halves

4. Make the number $\frac{1}{2}$ $\frac{1}{2}$

5. Make the answer to $\frac{1}{2} + \frac{1}{4}$ $\frac{3}{4}$

6. Show picture cards $\frac{1}{4}$ $\frac{2}{6}$

7. Write fraction sentences $\frac{1}{3} + \frac{1}{6} = \frac{1}{2}$

8. Make equivalent sentences. $\frac{2}{6} = \frac{1}{3}$

Inside-Outside Circle

Students stand in two concentric circles, with the inside circle facing out and outside circle facing in. They make a quarter turn right. Teacher tells them how many to rotate; they face a partner and share information.

Teacher Directed

Answers

1. Show Fraction cards: $\boxed{\dfrac{2}{5} + \dfrac{1}{5} =}$

$\dfrac{1}{4}, \dfrac{1}{3}, \dfrac{3}{5}$

2. What is the lowest equivalent fraction of $\dfrac{2}{4}$?

$\dfrac{1}{2}$

3. Show both fractions. Which is greater?

$\dfrac{1}{2}$ or $\dfrac{1}{3}$

$\dfrac{1}{2}$

4. Add both fractions $\dfrac{1}{2} + \dfrac{1}{4}$. What is their total?

Flashcard Directed

Each student has a flashcard with the problem on the front and the answer on the back. After asking their partner, they trade cards and then rotate with their new card to a new partner.

Front

Back

Sample:

Question:
$\dfrac{2}{3} + \dfrac{1}{6} = \underline{\quad}$

Answer:
$\dfrac{5}{6}$

Line-Ups

Students line up in a given order.

1. Select one fraction, line up smallest to largest.
2. Trade fractions, line up again smallest to largest.
3. Write a fraction on paper, line up smallest to largest.
4. Select 2 fraction pieces, add them together and line up your answer.
5. Line up, and figure out class fraction
   - boys-girls
   - pants-dresses
   - glasses/no glasses
   - laced shoes, non-laced shoes

Mix-Freeze-Group

Students "Mill and Mingle" around the room until the teacher calls "Freeze". The teacher then poses a problem which has a number for an answer. Students then rush to huddle in groups with the correct number.

Students select 1 fraction piece and teacher says:
1. Form groups equal to 1 using your fraction pieces.
2. Form groups equal to ½ using your fraction pieces.
3. Form groups equal to ¾ using your fraction pieces.

Teacher poses problems, no fraction pieces are used:
4. ½ + ¼ = How many ¼ths does that equal (3)
5. One whole - 2/4. How many ¼ths are left (2)
6. 5/6 - 2/6 = How many 6th are left? (3)

Similarity Groups

Teacher announces the dimension. Students record their preference on a sheet of paper. Students circulate and attempt to find those who have the same answer. Everyone with the same answer forms a group. Remember to have a group called "other."

Select one fraction from your kit:

1. Draw a loaf of bread. Divide it into sections and shade 3 slices.
2. Draw a pizza. Divide it into sections and shade 2 pieces.
3. Group—same exact fraction
4. Group so that all equivalent fractions are together.

Let's Build One

▶ **Concept:** Naming Fractions and finding all possible ways to build 1.

▶ **Level:** *Concrete*

▶ **Materials:** Fraction Bars

▶ **Structure:** RallyTable

Student pairs start with 1 whole bar in front of them. Teacher says "Take turns using pieces from both of your sets and build _**"1 whole bar"**_ as many different ways as you can." Each student builds and explains to his/her partner the answer.

Step
1 "A" places pieces and says "½ + ½".

Step
2 "B" places pieces and says "½, ⅛, ⅛, ¼."

1				1.00
1/2 .500		1/2 .500		
1/2 .500	1/8 .125	1/8 .125	1/4 .250	

Step
3 A goes next.

Students continue until they have placed all their fraction pieces.

Let's Draw One

▶ **Concept:** Naming Fractions by drawing and numbers.

▶ **Level:** *Connecting*

▶ **Materials:** "Let's Draw 1" recording worksheets per pair

▶ **Structure:** RallyTable

Students work with a partner, taking turns. They use a copy of the recording sheet provided on the next page. One student draws fractions that fit in the whole, then writes the correct size fraction inside the piece. Next, they name the pieces. The other student watches, coaches (if needed) and praises.

Step

1

"A" Draws	Writes	Names
	1	"1"

"B" watches, coaches if needed, and praises

Step

2

"B" Draws	Writes	Names
	$\frac{1}{2}$ $\frac{1}{4}$ $\frac{1}{4}$	"½, ¼, ¼ = 1"

"A" watches, coaches if needed, and praises.

Step

3 Students continue taking turns.

Laurie Kagan: *Fraction Fun*
Kagan Publishing • 1 (800) 933-2667 • www.KaganOnline.com

Let's Draw One

W O R K S H E E T

Instructions: Taking turns, draw and label ways to build one.

Sample:

½	¼	¼

A. _____   **B.** _____
         Name   Name

RallyTable

A	
B	
A	
B	
A	
B	
A	
B	
A	
B	
A	
B	
A	
B	

Laurie Kagan: *Fraction Fun*

Kagan Publishing • 1 (800) 933-2667 • www.KaganOnline.com

Ways to Write One

▶ **Concept:** Naming Fractions as we write one.

▶ **Level:** *Symbolic*

▶ **Materials:** Blank Paper

▶ **Structure:** RallyTable, Pairs Compare

Challenge pairs to work with just numbers and come up with as many different ways to write the fractions that sum to 1. Take turns recording the numbers on one sheet of paper.

Step
"A" writes fraction pieces that equal 1.
Sample: 1 = ½ + ½

Step
"B" checks and praises. (If they are not sure, they use their fraction bars and build the fractions to check the answer.)

Step
"B" writes fraction pieces that equal 1. **Sample:** 1 = ⅛, ⅛, ⅛, ⅛, ½

Step
"A" checks and praises.

Continue until the teacher says "STOP". Pairs compare with another pair. They ask which solutions both pairs found, and which were unique to each pair. They use the Pairs Compare worksheet on the following page.

Sample

| Names: | A._____ |
| | B._____ |

A   1 = ½, ½
B   1 = ⅛, ⅛, ⅛, ⅛, ½
A

Ways To Write One

Names   A. _____

B. _____

A. 1 = _____

B. 1 = _____

A. 1 = _____

B. 1 = _____

A. 1 = _____

B. 1 = _____

A. 1 = _____

B. 1 = _____

A. 1 = _____

B. 1 = _____

A. 1 = _____

B. 1 = _____

A. 1 = _____

B. 1 = _____

A. 1 = _____

B. 1 = _____

Ways To Write One

WORKSHEET

Pairs Compare

Pair 1

_____

_____

_____

_____

Neither

Both

_____

_____

_____

_____

_____

_____

_____

_____

_____

Pair 2

_____

_____

_____

_____

Laurie Kagan: *Fraction Fun*
Kagan Publishing • 1 (800) 933-2667 • www.KaganOnline.com

Race to One

▶ **Concept:** Naming Fractions as we build the whole.

▶ **Level:** *Concrete*

▶ **Materials:** 4 individual Fraction Kits, Concrete Dice

▶ **Structure:** **RoundTable**

Step 1

Student 1 rolls the dice and finds the corresponding fraction and places it on top of the whole bar.

Sample:

Person 1's Whole Strip

#1 rolls 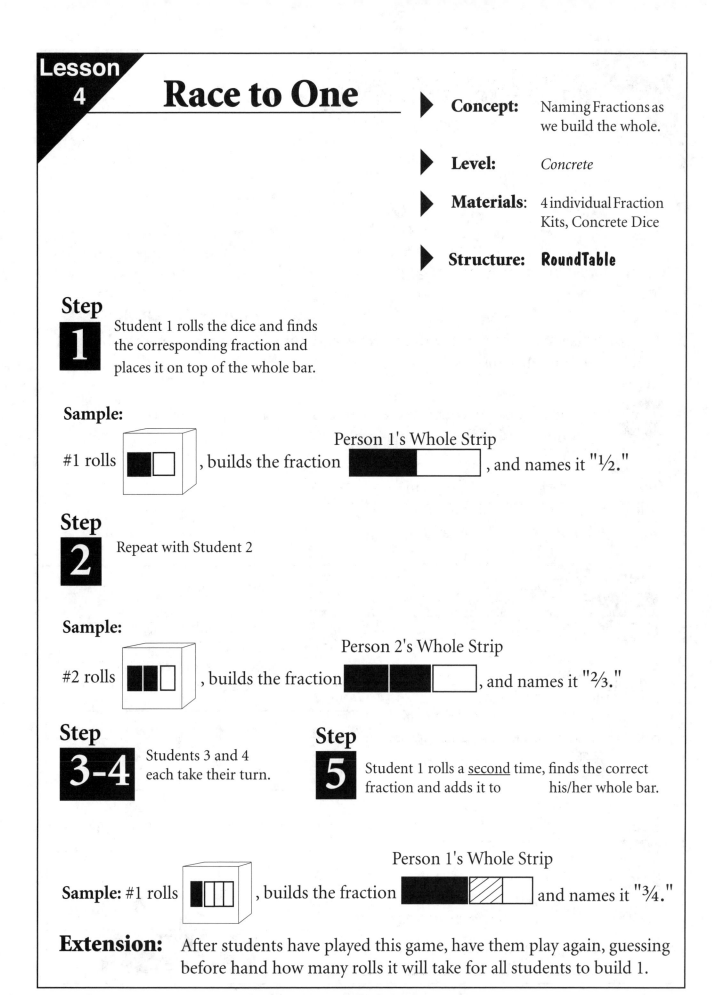, builds the fraction , and names it "½."

Step 2

Repeat with Student 2

Sample:

Person 2's Whole Strip

#2 rolls , builds the fraction , and names it "⅔."

Step 3-4

Students 3 and 4 each take their turn.

Step 5

Student 1 rolls a <u>second</u> time, finds the correct fraction and adds it to his/her whole bar.

Person 1's Whole Strip

Sample: #1 rolls , builds the fraction and names it "¾."

Extension:

After students have played this game, have them play again, guessing before hand how many rolls it will take for all students to build 1.

Lesson 5 — Racing to Write One

Concept: Naming Fractions by rolling dice and building a whole with drawings and labels.

Level: *Connecting*

Materials: 1 Recording Worksheet per team, Concrete Dice, Fraction Bars

Structure: RoundTable

The students record the game with drawings and numbers on four separate sheets of paper. Use Game 1 strips first.

Step 1

Student #1 rolls the concrete die, then draws and labels the fraction bar on the handout using the 1st game strip.

Sample:

Teammember #1 rolls and draws in the fraction pieces and labels.

Game 1

$\frac{1}{3}$	

Step 2-4

Continue; Teammates 2, 3, 4 each roll and record on their separate sheets.

Sample:

Teammember #1 rolls and draws in the fraction pieces and labels.

Step 5

Student #1 rolls again, draws and labels on his/her new fraction on <u>same</u> recording strip (Game 1).

Game 2

$\frac{1}{3}$	$\frac{1}{4}$	$\frac{1}{4}$	

Manipulatives can be placed so student knows where to draw the line.

$\frac{1}{3}$	$\frac{1}{4}$	$\frac{1}{4}$	

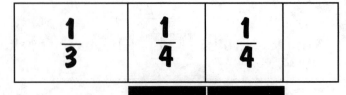

Step 6

Continue RoundTable. A player must roll exactly what is needed to build the whole.

Extension: Use the symbolic dice.

Laurie Kagan: *Fraction Fun*
Kagan Publishing • 1 (800) 933-2667 • www.KaganOnline.com

Racing To Write One

WORKSHEET

Instructions: Each student in turn rolls a die, draws the fraction, and names it. (Cut apart on the dotted lines, pass out 1 to each teammember.)

Person 1

Game 1

Game 2

Person 2

Game 1

Game 2

Person 3

Game 1

Game 2

Person 4

Game 1

Game 2

Rolling One

▶ **Concept:** Naming Fractions by rolling dice and building a whole with numbers.

▶ **Level:** *Symbolic*

▶ **Materials:** 1 Recording Worksheet per team, Symbolic Die

▶ **Structure:** **RoundTable**

At this level all four students record on one sheet of paper using the RoundTable structure. Each student now rolls the symbolic die and records how he/she will get to 1.

Step 1
#1 rolls $\frac{3}{4}$ and writes that fraction by his/her number.

Step 2
#2 rolls $\frac{1}{2}$ and writes that fraction by her number.

Sample

Person 1	$^3/_4$
Person 2	$^1/_2$
Person 3	
Person 4	

Step 3
#3 rolls and writes.

Step 4
#4 rolls and writes.

Step 5
Continue RoundTable. Each time the students add the fraction rolled if they can. If the fraction rolled is too large (makes them go over), they pass and its next players rolls.

Sample
#1 rolls $\frac{1}{8}$ and adds it to her first fraction

Person 1	$^3/_4 + ^1/_8$
Person 2	$^1/_2$
Person 3	$^1/_8$
Person 4	$^1/_2$

Variations:
• Build $^1/_2$ or $^2/_3$ of a whole.
• Start with fraction covers
• Use a cooperative format. Have teams work to beat their own record. (Build the number in fewer rolls.)

Rolling One

WORKSHEET

Instructions: Each student in a team rolls and records the outcome. Keep rolling until each student reaches 1 whole.

RoundTable

Team Name _____

_____ _____ _____ _____
#1   #2   #3   #4

Game 1

Person 1 _____

Person 2 _____

Person 3 _____

Person 4 _____

Game 2

Person 1 _____

Person 2 _____

Person 3 _____

Person 4 _____

Roll & Compare

Concept: Comparing Fractions

Level: *Concrete*

Materials: 4 Role cards per team, Fraction bars, Concrete Dice

Structure: **RoundTable with Rotating Roles**

Before you start:
Each teammmember makes or receives a role card.

#1= 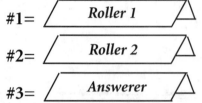 *Roller 1*

#2= *Roller 2*

#3= *Answerer*

#4= *Checker & Praiser*

(Fold index card lengthwise and add the same role name to the front and back of each card.)

To start, each team needs to lay out two "whole" fraction bars to build on.

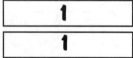

1
1

Step 1

"Roller #1" **rolls, builds** (finds corresponding fraction and lays it on top of the whole) and **names** the fraction out loud to his/her teammates.

Sample: rolls   builds   names

   "This is ½."

Step 2

"Roller #2" **rolls, builds** on the 2nd whole piece and names the fraction.

Sample: rolls   builds   names

   "This is ¾."

Step 3

Answerer says which is greater, (Sample: "¾ is greater than ½.")

Step 4

Checker and Praiser look to see if he is correct and praise the answer. (Sample: "That's right! ¾ is greater than ½. Good comparison work.")

Step 5

Rotate "role cards" clockwise and continue playing, starting with Step 1 so that each student plays every role. Continue until the teacher says "STOP."

Which is Greater?

Concept: Comparing Fractions

Level: *Connecting*

Materials: 2 spinners per team, Fraction bars, 1 worksheet per team

Structure: **RoundTable with Rotating Roles**

Before you start:
Each teammember makes a role card.

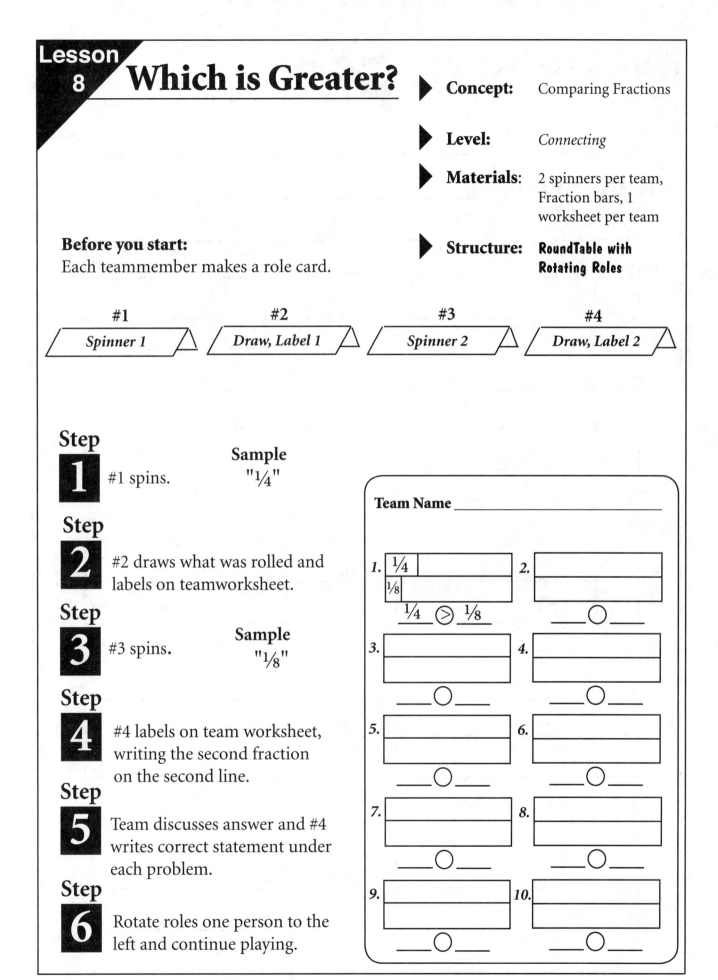

#1 | Spinner 1
#2 | Draw, Label 1
#3 | Spinner 2
#4 | Draw, Label 2

Step 1 #1 spins.　Sample "1/4"

Step 2 #2 draws what was rolled and labels on teamworksheet.

Step 3 #3 spins.　Sample "1/8"

Step 4 #4 labels on team worksheet, writing the second fraction on the second line.

Step 5 Team discusses answer and #4 writes correct statement under each problem.

Step 6 Rotate roles one person to the left and continue playing.

Team Name _____

1. 1/4 | 1/8 　 1/4 ⊘ 1/8
2. ___ ◯ ___
3. ___ ◯ ___
4. ___ ◯ ___
5. ___ ◯ ___
6. ___ ◯ ___
7. ___ ◯ ___
8. ___ ◯ ___
9. ___ ◯ ___
10. ___ ◯ ___

Which is Greater

WORKSHEET

Team Name _____

1. [___] ___ ○ ___

2. [___] ___ ○ ___

3. [___] ___ ○ ___

4. [___] ___ ○ ___

5. [___] ___ ○ ___

6. [___] ___ ○ ___

7. [___] ___ ○ ___

8. [___] ___ ○ ___

9. [___] ___ ○ ___

10. [___] ___ ○ ___

Compare the Fractions

▶ **Concept:** Comparing Fractions Greater than, less than, equal to

▶ **Level:** *Symbolic*

▶ **Materials:** 1 Pairs Check worksheet per pair, Fraction bars

▶ **Structure:** Pairs Check

Students work in pairs within their team. There is one Pairs ✓ Worksheet for each pair.

Step 1
A's do problem 1 (write >, < or = in the circle) B's watch, coach, and praise.

Step 2
B's do problem 2, A's watch, coach, and praise.

Step 3
Pairs check with other pair across the table after every two problems. Teams celebrate if the first two are correct. If not, as a team they fix the problem, and then celebrate.

Step 4
Continue "Pairs Check" A's do 3, B's do 4, check, celebrate, and so on.

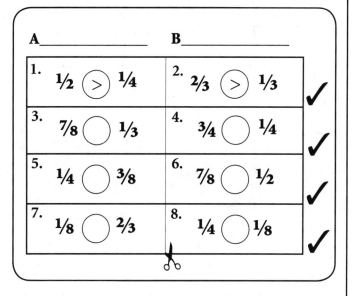

Notes: The " ✓ " mark on this side reminds students to celebrate. Trace over the " ✓" after they have checked two problems. ⊘ Circle the check after they celebrate their success.

Compare the Fractions

WORKSHEET

Instructions: Give the correct sign (<, >, or =) for each ◯.
(You may use your Fraction Bars to check.)

Pairs ✓

A _____   B _____

1. $\dfrac{1}{4}$ ◯ $\dfrac{1}{5}$		2. $\dfrac{1}{2}$ ◯ $\dfrac{2}{3}$		✓
3. $\dfrac{3}{4}$ ◯ $\dfrac{5}{6}$		4. $\dfrac{4}{5}$ ◯ $\dfrac{5}{8}$		✓
5. $\dfrac{3}{5}$ ◯ $\dfrac{2}{3}$		6. $\dfrac{1}{5}$ ◯ $\dfrac{3}{4}$		✓
7. $\dfrac{1}{2}$ ◯ $\dfrac{5}{8}$		8. $\dfrac{3}{8}$ ◯ $\dfrac{1}{2}$		✓
9. $\dfrac{3}{4}$ ◯ $\dfrac{2}{3}$		10. $\dfrac{2}{5}$ ◯ $\dfrac{2}{3}$		✓
11. $\dfrac{1}{3}$ ◯ $\dfrac{1}{2}$		12. $\dfrac{7}{12}$ ◯ $\dfrac{2}{3}$		✓
13. $\dfrac{7}{10}$ ◯ $\dfrac{3}{4}$		14. $\dfrac{3}{8}$ ◯ $\dfrac{2}{5}$		✓
15. $\dfrac{3}{4}$ ◯ $\dfrac{3}{5}$		16. $\dfrac{1}{2}$ ◯ $\dfrac{7}{8}$		✓
17. $\dfrac{1}{4}$ ◯ $\dfrac{1}{3}$		18. $\dfrac{1}{8}$ ◯ $\dfrac{3}{16}$		✓
19. $\dfrac{5}{8}$ ◯ $\dfrac{2}{3}$		20. $\dfrac{3}{4}$ ◯ $\dfrac{4}{5}$		✓

Laurie Kagan: *Fraction Fun*
Kagan Publishing • 1 (800) 933-2667 • www.KaganOnline.com

What Matches Up?

Concept: Equivalent Fractions

Level: *Concrete*

Materials: Transparency Fraction Spinner, Fraction bars, Overhead Projector

Structure: **Think-Build-Pair-Square**

Before you start: Each student starts with his/her whole bar in front of them.

Step 1

Think: Teacher spins the transparency spinner and says "Find your ½ fraction piece and lay it down on your whole bar in front of you. **Think** of the pieces in your fraction kit, what are some pieces that are equivalent to ½?"

Step 2

Build: Build on your ½ piece an equivalent to ½. All students work this problem out at the same time.

Sample: Student #1 ▮▮▮▮☐ (4/8)

Step 3

Pair: Check with your partner. Look to see if your pieces are the same length. If they are not equivalent, help each other until they are.

Sample: Student #1 ▮▮▮▮☐ (4/8)

Student #2 ▮▮☐ (2/4)

Step 4

Square: Share all the different equivalent fractions you found. Also, see if you can build any others.

Sample:
#1 ▮▮▮☐ (4/8)
#2 ▮▮☐ (2/4)
#3 ▮▮▮▮☐ (5/10)
#4 ▮▮☐ (2/4)

Team Discussion:
"Number 2 and Number 4 are the same. How about 16th's? Are there any others? Let's see what else we can figure out."

Step 5

Continue playing and building by repeating Steps 1-4.

Even Line Ups

▶ **Concept:** Equivalent Fractions

▶ **Level:** *Connecting*

▶ **Materials:** Symbolic Dice, 1 worksheet per pair, Fraction Bars

▶ **Structure:** RallyTable

Step 1

"A" rolls the symbolic die, and records the fraction ave the line that says "dice."

Step 2

"A and B" **discuss, draw and label** all the possibilities, taking turns. They may use their fraction bars to figure out the answers.

Step 3

Continue playing, taking turns of who starts.

Sample

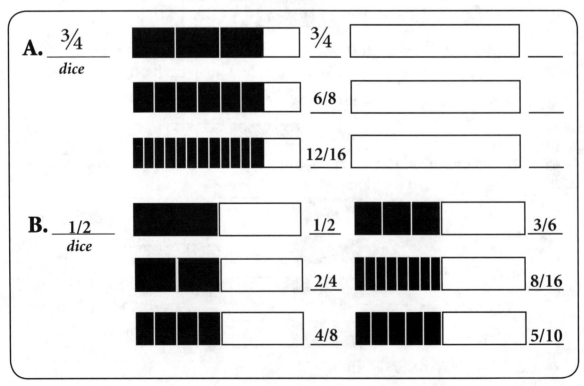

Laurie Kagan: *Fraction Fun*
Kagan Publishing • 1 (800) 933-2667 • www.KaganOnline.com

Even Line Ups

WORKSHEET

Instructions: Roll the dice and draw and label all the possible equivalent fractions.

A. _____

B. _____

A. _____
dice

B. _____
dice

A. _____
dice

B. _____
dice

Laurie Kagan: *Fraction Fun*

Equivalents

▶ **Concept:** Equivalent Fractions

▶ **Level:** *Symbolic*

▶ **Materials:** 1 Pair Check Worksheet per pair

▶ **Structure:** **Pairs Check**

Students work in pairs within their team. There is one Pairs Check worksheet for each pair.

Sample Worksheet

A_____ B_____

1. $\dfrac{1}{4} = \dfrac{2}{8} = \dfrac{4}{16}$	2. $\dfrac{1}{2} = \dfrac{2}{4} = \dfrac{4}{8} = \dfrac{8}{16}$ ✓
3. $\dfrac{1}{3} =$	4. $\dfrac{12}{16} =$ ✓
5. $\dfrac{3}{4} =$	6. $\dfrac{4}{8} =$ ✓

Step 1
A's do problem 1 (write >, < or = in the circle) B's watch, coach, and praise.

Step 2
B's do problem 2, A's watch, coach, and praise.

Step 3
Pairs check with other pair across the table after every two problems. Teams celebrate if the first two are correct. If not, as a team they fix the problem, and then celebrate.

Step 4
Continue "Pairs Check" A's do 3, B's do 4, check, celebrate, and so on.

Notes: The "✓" mark on this side reminds students to celebrate. Trace over the "✓" after they have checked two problems. Ⓥ Circle the check after they celebrate their success.

Equivalents

WORKSHEET

Instructions: Record all the possible equivalents.

Pairs ✓

A _____   B _____

1. $\dfrac{1}{4} =$	2. $\dfrac{1}{2} =$
3. $\dfrac{1}{3} =$	4. $\dfrac{12}{16} =$
5. $\dfrac{3}{4} =$	6. $\dfrac{4}{8} =$
7. $\dfrac{4}{12} =$	8. $\dfrac{1}{5} =$
9. $\dfrac{2}{3} =$	10. $\dfrac{3}{5} =$
11. $\dfrac{6}{8} =$	12. $\dfrac{2}{6} =$
13. $\dfrac{3}{6} =$	14. $\dfrac{8}{12} =$
15. $\dfrac{3}{12} =$	16. $\dfrac{4}{16} =$

Add On

▶ **Concept:**   Addition of Fractions

▶ **Level:**   *Concrete*

▶ **Materials**:   Concrete Die, Fraction Bars

▶ **Structure:**   **RallyRobin, RallyTable**

Before you start: Each pair places 1 whole fraction bar in front of them.

Step 1

"A" rolls the <u>concrete</u> die and builds that fraction on the whole.

Sample: "A" rolls and builds
½ on top of whole bar

Step 2

"B" rolls the concrete die and adds that fraction piece to the end of the first piece.

Sample: "B" rolls and adds ¼ to the ½ that is already built.

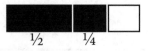

Step 3

"A" says the whole problem and answer. They may use the fraction bars to figure out the answer.

Sample: ½ + ¼ = ¾

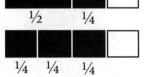

Step 4

"B" checks by placing the answer underneath their problem and checks to make sure its an exact match. Then "B" praises.

Step 5

Switch roles. "B" starts, "A" adds, "B" answers, and "A" checks and praises. Continue until it's time to stop.

Denominator Match

Concept: Addition of Fractions

Level: *Connecting*

Materials: 2 spinners, 1 Denominator Match Worksheet per pair, 1 Cut & Paste Fraction Worksheet per pair, glue or tape.

Structure: RallyTable

Before you start: a. Xerox one page for each pair.
b. Have each team cut apart small fractions on page.

Step 1

"A" spins the spinner and builds that fraction with manipulative pieces.

Sample: "A" pastes ³⁄₈ on worksheet.

| $\frac{1}{8}$ | $\frac{1}{8}$ | $\frac{1}{8}$ | | |

Step 2

"B" **adds** the second fraction onto the original fraction.

| $\frac{1}{8}$ | $\frac{1}{8}$ | $\frac{1}{8}$ | $\frac{1}{4}$ | |

Sample: "B" pastes ¼ onto the same worksheet.

Step 3

"A" and "B" figure out with manipulatives what the common denominator is and glue it below the problem to show how to solve the problem.

Problem
| $\frac{1}{8}$ | $\frac{1}{8}$ | $\frac{1}{8}$ | $\frac{1}{4}$ | |
"problem"

Answer
| $\frac{1}{8}$ | $\frac{1}{8}$ | $\frac{1}{8}$ | $\frac{1}{8}$ | $\frac{1}{8}$ | |

Step 4

Show the steps with numbers. 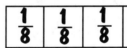 $\frac{3}{8} + \frac{1}{4} = \frac{3}{8} + \frac{2}{8} = \frac{5}{8}$

Denominator Match

WORKSHEET

A _____   B _____

Show your work with manipulatives and numbers.

1. $\dfrac{1}{2} + \dfrac{1}{6}$ **Answer** _____

2. $\dfrac{3}{4} + \dfrac{1}{8}$ **Answer** _____

3. $\dfrac{2}{3} + \dfrac{1}{6}$ **Answer** _____

4. $\dfrac{5}{8} + \dfrac{3}{4}$ **Answer** _____

Laurie Kagan: *Fraction Fun*

Kagan Publishing • 1 (800) 933-2667 • www.KaganOnline.com

Denominator Match

WORKSHEET

Cut & Paste Fraction Pieces

1

1

$\frac{1}{2}$	$\frac{1}{2}$

$\frac{1}{2}$	$\frac{1}{2}$

$\frac{1}{3}$	$\frac{1}{3}$	$\frac{1}{3}$

$\frac{1}{3}$	$\frac{1}{3}$	$\frac{1}{3}$

$\frac{1}{4}$	$\frac{1}{4}$	$\frac{1}{4}$	$\frac{1}{4}$

$\frac{1}{4}$	$\frac{1}{4}$	$\frac{1}{4}$	$\frac{1}{4}$

$\frac{1}{5}$	$\frac{1}{5}$	$\frac{1}{5}$	$\frac{1}{5}$	$\frac{1}{5}$

$\frac{1}{5}$	$\frac{1}{5}$	$\frac{1}{5}$	$\frac{1}{5}$	$\frac{1}{5}$

$\frac{1}{6}$	$\frac{1}{6}$	$\frac{1}{6}$	$\frac{1}{6}$	$\frac{1}{6}$	$\frac{1}{6}$

$\frac{1}{6}$	$\frac{1}{6}$	$\frac{1}{6}$	$\frac{1}{6}$	$\frac{1}{6}$	$\frac{1}{6}$

$\frac{1}{8}$	$\frac{1}{8}$	$\frac{1}{8}$	$\frac{1}{8}$	$\frac{1}{8}$	$\frac{1}{8}$	$\frac{1}{8}$	$\frac{1}{8}$

$\frac{1}{8}$	$\frac{1}{8}$	$\frac{1}{8}$	$\frac{1}{8}$	$\frac{1}{8}$	$\frac{1}{8}$	$\frac{1}{8}$	$\frac{1}{8}$

$\frac{1}{10}$	$\frac{1}{10}$	$\frac{1}{10}$	$\frac{1}{10}$	$\frac{1}{10}$	$\frac{1}{10}$	$\frac{1}{10}$	$\frac{1}{10}$	$\frac{1}{10}$	$\frac{1}{10}$

$\frac{1}{10}$	$\frac{1}{10}$	$\frac{1}{10}$	$\frac{1}{10}$	$\frac{1}{10}$	$\frac{1}{10}$	$\frac{1}{10}$	$\frac{1}{10}$	$\frac{1}{10}$	$\frac{1}{10}$

$\frac{1}{12}$	$\frac{1}{12}$	$\frac{1}{12}$	$\frac{1}{12}$	$\frac{1}{12}$	$\frac{1}{12}$	$\frac{1}{12}$	$\frac{1}{12}$	$\frac{1}{12}$	$\frac{1}{12}$	$\frac{1}{12}$	$\frac{1}{12}$

$\frac{1}{12}$	$\frac{1}{12}$	$\frac{1}{12}$	$\frac{1}{12}$	$\frac{1}{12}$	$\frac{1}{12}$	$\frac{1}{12}$	$\frac{1}{12}$	$\frac{1}{12}$	$\frac{1}{12}$	$\frac{1}{12}$	$\frac{1}{12}$

$\frac{1}{16}$	$\frac{1}{16}$	$\frac{1}{16}$	$\frac{1}{16}$	$\frac{1}{16}$	$\frac{1}{16}$	$\frac{1}{16}$	$\frac{1}{16}$	$\frac{1}{16}$	$\frac{1}{16}$	$\frac{1}{16}$	$\frac{1}{16}$	$\frac{1}{16}$	$\frac{1}{16}$	$\frac{1}{16}$	$\frac{1}{16}$

$\frac{1}{16}$	$\frac{1}{16}$	$\frac{1}{16}$	$\frac{1}{16}$	$\frac{1}{16}$	$\frac{1}{16}$	$\frac{1}{16}$	$\frac{1}{16}$	$\frac{1}{16}$	$\frac{1}{16}$	$\frac{1}{16}$	$\frac{1}{16}$	$\frac{1}{16}$	$\frac{1}{16}$	$\frac{1}{16}$	$\frac{1}{16}$

Laurie Kagan: *Fraction Fun*

Kagan Publishing • 1 (800) 933-2667 • www.KaganOnline.com

Adding Fractions

▶ **Concept:** Addition of Fractions

▶ **Level:** *Symbolic*

▶ **Materials:** 1 Pairs Check Worksheet per pair

▶ **Structure:** Pairs Check

Common Denominator

Step Add the numerators.

Step 2 Reduce to lowest terms.

Uncommon Denominator

Step Find the common denominator.

Step 2 Add the numerators.

Sample

1. $\dfrac{1}{6}+\dfrac{3}{6}=\dfrac{4}{6}=\dfrac{2}{3}$	2. $\dfrac{2}{4}+\dfrac{1}{4}=\dfrac{3}{4}$ ✓
3. $\dfrac{3}{5}+\dfrac{1}{5}=\dfrac{4}{5}$	4. $\dfrac{1}{3}+\dfrac{1}{3}=\dfrac{2}{3}$ ✓
5.	6. ✓

Sample

1. $\begin{aligned}\dfrac{1}{3}&=\dfrac{3}{6}\\+\dfrac{2}{6}&=\dfrac{2}{6}\\\hline &\dfrac{5}{6}\end{aligned}$	2. $\begin{aligned}\dfrac{1}{4}&=\dfrac{3}{12}\\+\dfrac{1}{3}&=\dfrac{4}{12}\\\hline &\dfrac{7}{12}\end{aligned}$ ✓
3. $\begin{aligned}\dfrac{1}{2}&=\dfrac{5}{10}\\+\dfrac{2}{5}&=\dfrac{4}{10}\\\hline &\dfrac{9}{10}\end{aligned}$	4. $\begin{aligned}\dfrac{1}{4}&=\dfrac{1}{4}\\+\dfrac{1}{2}&=\dfrac{2}{4}\\\hline &\dfrac{3}{4}\end{aligned}$ ✓

Adding Fractions

Lesson 15

WORKSHEET

Addition (Common Denominator)

Pairs ✓

Instructions: Add, then reduce sums to lowest terms. **You must show your work.**

A _____ **B** _____

1. $\dfrac{1}{5} + \dfrac{2}{5} =$	2. $\dfrac{1}{3} + \dfrac{1}{3} =$
3. $\dfrac{1}{10} + \dfrac{7}{10} =$	4. $\dfrac{3}{8} + \dfrac{3}{8} =$
5. $\dfrac{1}{4} + \dfrac{2}{4} =$	6. $\dfrac{1}{6} + \dfrac{5}{6} =$
7. $\dfrac{3}{8} + \dfrac{1}{8} =$	8. $\dfrac{3}{10} + \dfrac{1}{10} =$
9. $\dfrac{2}{6} + \dfrac{2}{6} =$	10. $\dfrac{2}{4} + \dfrac{1}{4} =$
11. $\dfrac{5}{12} + \dfrac{1}{12} =$	12. $\dfrac{2}{8} + \dfrac{6}{8} =$
13. $\dfrac{2}{7} + \dfrac{3}{7} =$	14. $\dfrac{3}{4} + \dfrac{1}{4} =$
15. $\dfrac{5}{7} + \dfrac{1}{7} =$	16. $\dfrac{4}{8} + \dfrac{1}{8} =$
17. $\dfrac{1}{5} + \dfrac{3}{5} =$	18. $\dfrac{3}{7} + \dfrac{4}{7} =$
19. $\dfrac{2}{6} + \dfrac{1}{6} =$	20. $\dfrac{1}{4} + \dfrac{1}{4} =$
21. $\dfrac{1}{3} + \dfrac{2}{3} =$	22. $\dfrac{5}{10} + \dfrac{1}{10} =$

Adding Fractions

WORKSHEET

Addition (Uncommon Denominator) Pairs ✓

Instructions: Add, then reduce sums to lowest terms. **You must show your work.**

A _____ **B** _____

1. $\dfrac{2}{5}$ $+\dfrac{3}{10}$		**2.** $\dfrac{2}{3}$ $+\dfrac{1}{6}$	✓
3. $\dfrac{1}{4}$ $+\dfrac{3}{8}$		**4.** $\dfrac{1}{8}$ $+\dfrac{1}{4}$	✓
5. $\dfrac{1}{2}$ $+\dfrac{1}{6}$		**6.** $\dfrac{3}{4}$ $+\dfrac{1}{8}$	✓
7. $\dfrac{1}{3}$ $+\dfrac{1}{6}$		**8.** $\dfrac{1}{4}$ $+\dfrac{1}{2}$	✓
9. $\dfrac{1}{5}$ $+\dfrac{1}{2}$		**10.** $\dfrac{1}{3}$ $+\dfrac{1}{2}$	✓
11. $\dfrac{3}{4}$ $+\dfrac{1}{12}$		**12.** $\dfrac{3}{8}$ $+\dfrac{1}{2}$	✓

Taking Away

▶ **Concept:** Subtraction of Fractions

▶ **Level:** *Concrete*

▶ **Materials:** Fraction Bars

▶ **Structure:** **Think-Pair-Square**

<u>*Teachers Note:*</u> *Remember to have students work in the same denominator when you start.*

Step 1 **Think & Build:** Teacher says: "¾". Each student builds ¾ on his whole fraction bar.

Step 2 **Think & Build:** Teacher says: "Subtract ¼". Each student subtracts ¼ from their workboard.

Step 3 **Pair:** Teacher says: Check with your partner. Do your fraction bars match up? Explain how you solved the problem to your partner.

A

B

(Students Check)

Step 4 **Square:** (Choral response) " What is the answer to ¾ - ¼?" = Students check with their teammates and make sure everyone understood the answer.

Step 5 Continue with new problems.

Same Denominator: 1. $\frac{3}{4} - \frac{1}{4}$ 2. $\frac{5}{6} - \frac{1}{6}$ 3. $\frac{3}{5} - \frac{2}{5}$

Different Denominators: 1. $\frac{3}{8} - \frac{1}{4}$ 2. $\frac{7}{10} - \frac{2}{5}$ 3. $\frac{2}{4} - \frac{1}{8}$

Subtraction

▶ **Concept:** Subtraction of Fractions

▶ **Level:** *Connecting*

▶ **Materials:** 1 Worksheet per pair

▶ **Structure:** **RallyTable**

Step 1

Draw: Teacher says "3/8". Student "A" must draw 3/8 on the paper and label it.

Teacher says "Subtract 1/4". Student "A" must draw 1/4 below the first bar and label it. He/she must figure out what is left. Show their equivalent work.

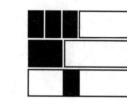

$$\frac{3}{8}$$
$$-\frac{1}{4}$$
$$\frac{1}{8}$$

$$\frac{3}{8} = \frac{3}{8}$$
$$-\frac{1}{4} = \frac{2}{8}$$
$$\overline{\frac{1}{8} = \frac{1}{8}}$$

Step 2

Check: "B" Help your partner as they are doing each problem. Does the drawing make sense? Do the numbers represent the drawings? Coach and help if needed.

Step 3

Praise: "B's" praise their "A" partners and get ready to do the next problem.

Step 4

Switch; continue with new problems.

Subtraction

WORKSHEET

A. _____   **B.** _____

1. $\frac{1}{2} - \frac{1}{4}$

2. $\frac{1}{3} - \frac{1}{6}$

3. $\frac{2}{5} - \frac{1}{10}$

4. $\frac{3}{4} - \frac{1}{8}$

5. $\frac{5}{6} - \frac{1}{3}$

6. $\frac{1}{2} - \frac{1}{3}$

7. $\frac{1}{4} - \frac{1}{6}$

8. $\frac{3}{5} - \frac{2}{10}$

Subtracting Fractions

▶ **Concept:** Subtraction of Fractions

▶ **Level:** *Symbolic*

▶ **Materials:** 1 Worksheet per pair

▶ **Structure:** **Pairs Check**

Each student works with their A,B partner and must check their worksheet with another pair after every two problems.

Common Denominator

Sample:

A _____ B _____

1. $\frac{3}{8} - \frac{1}{8} = \frac{2}{8} = \frac{1}{4}$	2. $\frac{4}{5} - \frac{1}{5} = \frac{3}{5}$ ✓
3. $\frac{3}{4} - \frac{1}{4} = \frac{2}{4} = \frac{1}{2}$	4. $\frac{5}{6} - \frac{2}{6} = \frac{3}{6} = \frac{1}{2}$ ✓
5. $\frac{7}{10} - \frac{2}{10} = \frac{5}{10} = \frac{1}{2}$	6. $\frac{2}{3} - \frac{1}{3} = \frac{1}{3}$ ✓
7. $\frac{5}{12} - \frac{1}{12} = \frac{4}{12} = \frac{1}{3}$	8. $\frac{15}{16} - \frac{12}{16} = \frac{3}{16}$ ✓

Uncommon Denominator

Sample:

A _____ B _____

1. $\frac{2}{3} = \frac{4}{6}$ $-\frac{1}{6} = \frac{1}{6}$ $\frac{3}{6} = \frac{1}{2}$	2. $\frac{1}{2} = \frac{2}{4}$ $-\frac{1}{4} = \frac{1}{4}$ $\frac{1}{4}$ ✓
3. $\frac{3}{4} = \frac{9}{12}$ $-\frac{1}{12} = \frac{1}{12}$ $\frac{8}{12} = \frac{4}{6} = \frac{2}{3}$	4. $\frac{2}{3} = \frac{8}{12}$ $-\frac{1}{4} = \frac{3}{12}$ $\frac{5}{12}$ ✓

Laurie Kagan: *Fraction Fun*
Kagan Publishing • 1 (800) 933-2667 • www.KaganOnline.com

Subtraction

WORKSHEET

Subtraction (Common Denominator)

Instructions: Reduce to lowest terms.

Pairs ✓

A _____   **B** _____

A	B	
1. $\dfrac{2}{3} - \dfrac{1}{3} =$	2. $\dfrac{5}{12} - \dfrac{1}{12} =$	✔
3. $\dfrac{4}{5} - \dfrac{2}{5} =$	4. $\dfrac{9}{10} - \dfrac{3}{10} =$	✔
5. $\dfrac{5}{6} - \dfrac{1}{6} =$	6. $\dfrac{3}{8} - \dfrac{2}{8} =$	✔
7. $\dfrac{4}{7} - \dfrac{2}{7} =$	8. $\dfrac{5}{9} - \dfrac{2}{9} =$	✔
9. $\dfrac{3}{8} - \dfrac{2}{8} =$	10. $\dfrac{11}{12} - \dfrac{4}{12} =$	✔
11. $\dfrac{3}{4} - \dfrac{1}{4} =$	12. $\dfrac{2}{5} - \dfrac{1}{5} =$	✔
13. $\dfrac{7}{10} - \dfrac{5}{10} =$	14. $\dfrac{7}{12} - \dfrac{5}{12} =$	✔
15. $\dfrac{5}{8} - \dfrac{3}{8} =$	16. $\dfrac{2}{9} - \dfrac{1}{9} =$	✔
17. $\dfrac{5}{6} - \dfrac{4}{6} =$	18. $\dfrac{7}{8} - \dfrac{5}{8} =$	✔
19. $\dfrac{11}{12} - \dfrac{7}{12} =$	20. $\dfrac{10}{12} - \dfrac{2}{12} =$	✔
21. $\dfrac{9}{11} - \dfrac{3}{11} =$	22. $\dfrac{3}{4} - \dfrac{2}{4} =$	✔

Laurie Kagan: *Fraction Fun*

Kagan Publishing • 1 (800) 933-2667 • www.KaganOnline.com

Subtraction

WORKSHEET

Subtraction (Uncommon Denominator)

Instructions: Find a common demonitor. Reduce to lowest terms.
You must show your work.

Pairs ✓

A _____ **B** _____

A	B
1. $\dfrac{5}{10}$ $-\dfrac{1}{5}$	**2.** $\dfrac{2}{3}$ $-\dfrac{1}{6}$
3. $\dfrac{3}{8}$ $-\dfrac{1}{4}$	**4.** $\dfrac{5}{8}$ $-\dfrac{1}{4}$
5. $\dfrac{1}{2}$ $-\dfrac{1}{6}$	**6.** $\dfrac{3}{4}$ $-\dfrac{1}{8}$
7. $\dfrac{1}{3}$ $-\dfrac{1}{6}$	**8.** $\dfrac{1}{2}$ $-\dfrac{1}{4}$
9. $\dfrac{7}{12}$ $-\dfrac{1}{6}$	**10.** $\dfrac{1}{2}$ $-\dfrac{2}{6}$

✓ ✓ ✓ ✓ ✓

Laurie Kagan: *Fraction Fun*
Kagan Publishing • 1 (800) 933-2667 • www.KaganOnline.com

Parts of a Fraction

Concept: Multiplication of Fractions

Level: *Concrete*

Materials: Fraction Bars

Structure: **Think-Pair-Share**

Teacher Note: ⅓ x ½ means "What is ⅓ of ½? To help students grasp the concept of multiplication by fractions, ask them if we start with a whole number like the fraction ½ x 8 = ½ of 8, the answer is 4; ½ x 2 = ½ of 2, the answer is 1.

Problem: ⅓ X ½

Step 1

Think: Build ½ on your fraction bar.

Build

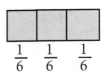

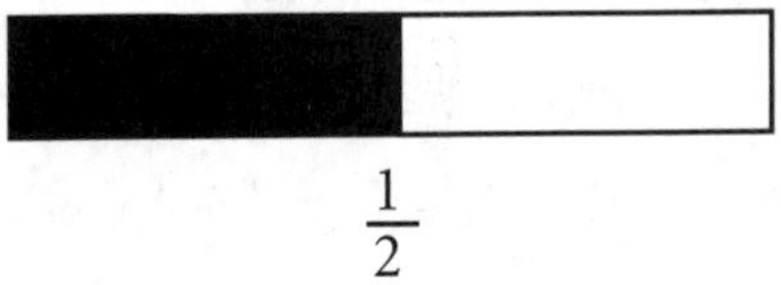

$\frac{1}{2}$

Step 2

Pair: Look closely and listen. What is the answer to ⅓ of ½? Pair with your partner and share your answer.

Build

$\frac{1}{6}$ $\frac{1}{6}$ $\frac{1}{6}$

Step 3

Share: Using "Choral Response" or "Slates," have all pairs share their answer.

Answer:

  $\frac{1}{6}$

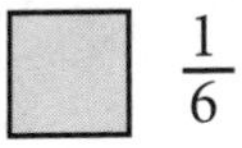

Sample Problems:

1. Problem: ¼ x ½ **Build:** ½ on your fraction bar **Find:** ¼ of the ½ **Answer:** ⅛		**2. Problem:** ¼ x ⅓ **Build:** ⅓ on your fraction bar **Find:** ¼ of the ⅓ **Answer:** 1/12
3. Problem: ½ x ⅔ **Build:** ⅔ on your fraction bar **Find:** ½ of the ⅔ **Answer:** ⅓		**4. Problem:** 1/6 x ½ **Build:** ½ on your fraction bar **Find:** 1/6 of the ½ **Answer:** 1/12

Finding Parts

▶ **Concept:** Multiplication of Fractions

▶ **Level:** *Connecting*

▶ **Materials:** 1 Pairs Check Worksheet per pair

▶ **Structure:** **Pairs Check**

Teacher's Note: *Model and check for understanding before starting worksheets.*

Sample 1:

Problem: ½ x ¼

A. Draw the whole into 4ths

B. Identify ¼ by shading

C. ½ of ¼ means break the ¼ in half by dotted lines

D. What is ½ of ¼?   ⅛

Draw

Shade

Break

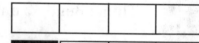

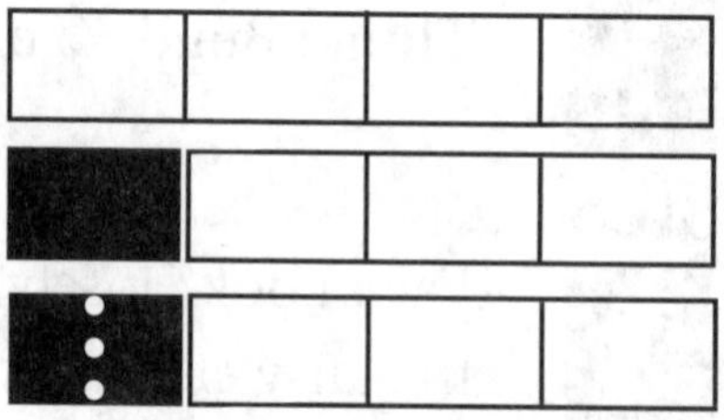

Problem: $\frac{1}{2} \times \frac{1}{4} = \frac{1 \times 1}{2 \times 4} = \frac{1}{8}$

Sample 2:

Problem: ½ x ¾

A. Draw the whole into 4ths

B. Identify ¾ by shading

C. ½ of ¾ means break the ¾ in half by dotted lines. 8ths will fit.

D. What is ½ of ¾?   ⅜

Draw

Shade

Break

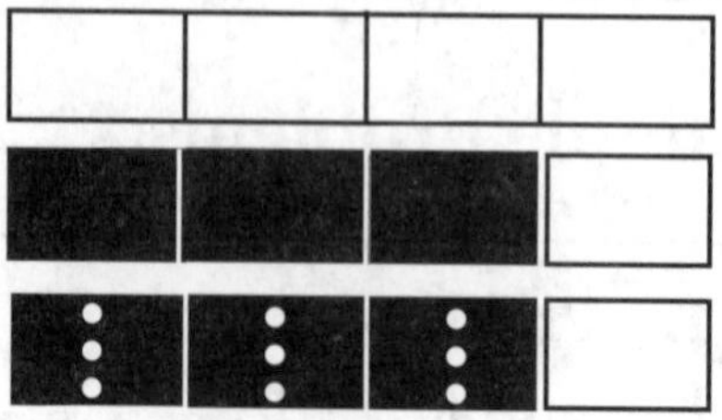

Problem: $\frac{1}{2} \times \frac{3}{4} = \frac{1 \times 3}{2 \times 4} = \frac{3}{8}$

Sample 3:

Problem: ⅓ x ¾

A. Draw the whole into 4ths

B. Identify ¾ by shading

C. ⅓ of ¾ means break the ¾ into 3rds by dotted lines.

D. What is ⅓ of ¾?   3/12 = ¼

Draw

Shade

Break

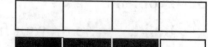

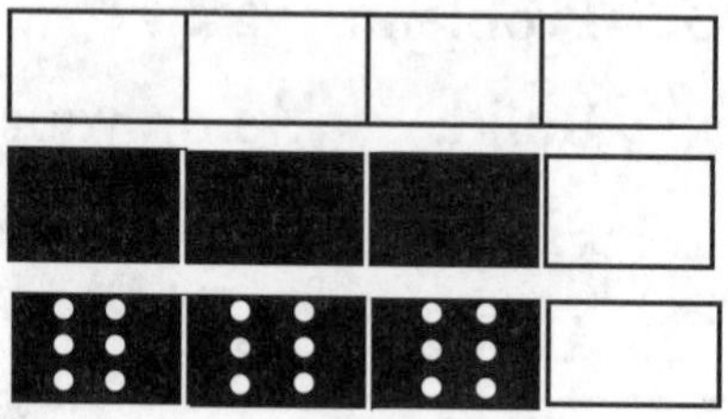

Problem: $\frac{1}{3} \times \frac{3}{4} = \frac{1 \times 3}{3 \times 4} = \frac{3}{12}$ or $\frac{1}{4}$

Finding Parts

WORKSHEET

Pairs ✓

A _____   B _____

1. $\dfrac{1}{6}$ x $\dfrac{1}{2}$

Draw

Shade

Break

Problem

2. $\dfrac{1}{3}$ x $\dfrac{1}{2}$

Draw

Shade

Break

Problem

✓

3. $\dfrac{1}{2}$ x $\dfrac{3}{5}$

Draw

Shade

Break

Problem

4. $\dfrac{1}{4}$ x $\dfrac{1}{2}$

Draw

Shade

Break

Problem

✓

5. $\dfrac{1}{3}$ x $\dfrac{1}{4}$

Draw

Shade

Break

Problem

6. $\dfrac{1}{5}$ x $\dfrac{2}{3}$

Draw

Shade

Break

Problem

✓

Laurie Kagan: *Fraction Fun*
Kagan Publishing • 1 (800) 933-2667 • www.KaganOnline.com

Multiplying Fractions

▶ **Concept:** Multiplication of Fractions

▶ **Level:** *Symbolic*

▶ **Materials:** 1 Pairs Check Worksheet per pair

▶ **Structure:** **Pairs Check**

Students work n pairs within their team.

Demonstrate how to do the problem showing all the steps.

Sample 1

$$\frac{1}{4} \times \frac{1}{2} = \frac{1 \times 1}{4 \times 2} = \frac{1}{8}$$

Sample 2

$$\frac{1}{3} \times \frac{3}{4} = \frac{1 \times 3}{3 \times 4} = \frac{3}{12} = \frac{1}{4}$$

Remind students that they must write out **all** of the steps and **reduce** to the lowest fraction.

Laurie Kagan: *Fraction Fun*
Kagan Publishing • 1 (800) 933-2667 • www.KaganOnline.com

Multiplying Fractions

WORKSHEET

(Common Denominator)
Instructions: Reduce to lowest terms. You must show all the steps!

Pairs ✓

A _____ **B** _____

1. $\dfrac{1}{2}$ x $\dfrac{1}{6}$ =	2. $\dfrac{1}{6}$ x $\dfrac{3}{4}$ =
3. $\dfrac{1}{3}$ x $\dfrac{1}{4}$ =	4. $\dfrac{1}{4}$ x $\dfrac{1}{5}$ =
5. $\dfrac{1}{6}$ x $\dfrac{2}{7}$ =	6. $\dfrac{1}{2}$ x $\dfrac{1}{3}$ =
7. $\dfrac{3}{4}$ x $\dfrac{1}{5}$ =	8. $\dfrac{4}{5}$ x $\dfrac{1}{2}$ =
9. $\dfrac{1}{2}$ x $\dfrac{1}{4}$ =	10. $\dfrac{1}{4}$ x $\dfrac{1}{2}$ =
11. $\dfrac{1}{5}$ x $\dfrac{3}{4}$ =	12. $\dfrac{2}{3}$ x $\dfrac{1}{4}$ =
13. $\dfrac{2}{3}$ x $\dfrac{1}{3}$ =	14. $\dfrac{3}{4}$ x $\dfrac{7}{8}$ =
15. $\dfrac{2}{5}$ x $\dfrac{1}{4}$ =	16. $\dfrac{1}{4}$ x $\dfrac{4}{5}$ =
17. $\dfrac{3}{8}$ x $\dfrac{1}{4}$ =	18. $\dfrac{5}{6}$ x $\dfrac{1}{7}$ =
19. $\dfrac{1}{6}$ x $\dfrac{3}{7}$ =	20. $\dfrac{1}{3}$ x $\dfrac{2}{5}$ =

How Many Fit

▶ **Concept:** Division of Fractions

▶ **Level:** *Concrete*

▶ **Materials:** Fraction Bars

▶ **Structure:** RallyTable

Teacher Note:

• $1 \div \frac{1}{2}$ means you are going to divide 1 by halves and see how many halves fit into 1.

• $\frac{1}{2} \div \frac{1}{4}$ means you are going to divide $\frac{1}{2}$ by fourths and see how many fit into $\frac{1}{2}$. Verbally the teacher gives problems.

• Students always start with the whole fraction bar in front of them.

• The teacher states problems and the students take turns solving them.

Sample 1 $\frac{1}{2} \div \frac{1}{4}$ **Sample:** "A's" build

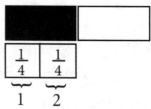

Step 1 "A's" put the $\frac{1}{2}$ fraction bar underneath whole fraction bar.

Step 2 Using $\frac{1}{4}$'s "A's" find out how many $\frac{1}{4}$ths can fit into the $\frac{1}{2}$ fraction bar by placing them below it.

Step 3 Ask the question. "One half divided by one fourth equals"
        "A's" Answer = "2"

Steps 4-6 Switch roles. "A" watches and checks while "B" solves the problem.

More Samples

2. $\frac{2}{3} \div \frac{1}{3}$

Answer = 2

3. $\frac{2}{3} \div \frac{1}{6}$

Answer = 4

Showing Division

▶ **Concept:** Division of Fractions

▶ **Level:** *Connecting*

▶ **Materials:** Showing Division Worksheet

▶ **Structure:** **Think-Pair-Share**

The teacher states the problem.

Sample 1:

Teacher says "One divided by one half equals?"

Students do 3 steps:

1. Write what the problem means.

   (1) **How many halfs fit into 1?**

2. Draw a picture.

   (2) 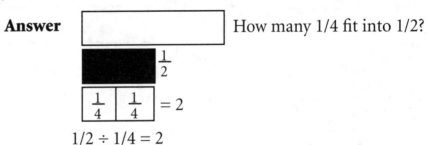 "2"

3. Write the problem in symbols.

   (3) $1 \div \dfrac{1}{2} = 2$

Sample 2:

Teacher says "1/2 ÷ 1/4 "

Students invidually write what the problem means, draw a picture and write the problem in symbols each time. When they have completed all 3 steps they check with their partner, then with their teammates.

Answer How many 1/4 fit into 1/2?

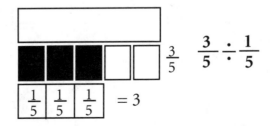

$1/2 \div 1/4 = 2$

Sample 3: $\dfrac{3}{5} \div \dfrac{1}{5}$ How many 1/5 fit into 3/5?

$\dfrac{3}{5} \div \dfrac{1}{5}$

Showing Division

WORKSHEET

Remember to do all 3 steps.

1. Write what the problem means.
2. Draw a picture.
3. Write the problem in numbers.

A. $\dfrac{1}{2} \div \dfrac{1}{4}$ How many _____ fit into _____?

B. $\dfrac{5}{6} \div \dfrac{1}{2}$ How many _____ fit into _____?

A. $\dfrac{3}{4} \div \dfrac{5}{8}$ How many _____ fit into _____?

B. $\dfrac{2}{3} \div \dfrac{3}{4}$ How many _____ fit into _____?

Invert & Multiply — Explaining Why

In lessons 22 and 23 students obtain an understanding of what it means to divide a fraction by a fraction. They see we are asking how many of one sized fraction fit into another. In the next three lessons they learn why, when dividing one fraction by another, it always works to "Invert and Multiply." For students to understand this procedure takes some direct instruction and a set of experiences at the concrete, connecting, and symbolic levels.

The rest of this page provides the basis for the direct instruction. The lessons which follow provide practice at the concrete, connecting, and symbolic levels, so students gain an experiential understanding of the symbolic operations involved as we "Invert and Multiply."

Direct Instruction:

When we are faced with a simple fraction division problem such as $\frac{1}{2} \div \frac{1}{4}$, it is easy to see that the answer is two. When we are faced with a more complex problem, such as $\frac{3}{4} \div \frac{1}{16}$ it is not as easy to do the problem in our head. Thus we need a set of operations to calculate the answer. A set of operations is called an algorithm.

The most common algorithm we use for dividing a fraction by a fraction is to "Invert and Multiply." Thus, $\frac{3}{4} \div \frac{1}{16} = \frac{3}{4} \times \frac{16}{1} = \frac{48}{4} = 12$. To understand why it always works to invert and multiply, lets examine what we are doing as we go through the steps.

Lets start with a simple problem like $\frac{1}{2} \div \frac{1}{4}$. One fourth is the divisor (or denominator), and $\frac{1}{2}$ is the dividend (or numerator). When we are faced with this problem we cannot divide in the same way as we divide whole numbers. If we write $\frac{1}{4} \overline{)\frac{1}{2}}$ we would not know what to do. We can solve this problem by enlarging the divisor $\left(\frac{1}{4}\right)$ to 1, because anything divided by one is always itself. But if we enlarge the divisor to one, we also have to enlarge the dividend. If we keep the same proportions between the two fractions, the fractions will be larger, but the same number of one will fit in another. It is just like looking at the fractions through a magnifying glass. As long as we enlarge one just as much as the other, we have not changed the relation between the two of them, and the answer to our division problem will be the same.

How do we make the divisor equal to one? Well, lets look carefully at $\frac{1}{2} \div \frac{1}{4}$. What will it take to make the $\frac{1}{4}$ equal to one? We need to multiply the $\frac{1}{4}$ by $\frac{4}{1}$, its reciprocal. And to keep the proportions right, we must multiple the numerator by $\frac{4}{1}$ also. So, when we see $\frac{1}{2} \div \frac{1}{4}$ we multiply both the $\frac{1}{2}$ and the $\frac{1}{4}$ by $\frac{4}{1}$. Thus, $\frac{1}{2} \div \frac{1}{4}$ becomes $\frac{1}{2} \times \frac{4}{1} \div \frac{1}{4} \times \frac{4}{1}$. Since $\frac{1}{4} \times \frac{4}{1}$ equals 1, our problem becomes $\frac{1}{2} \times \frac{4}{1} \div 1$. And since anything divided by one is itself, our problem becomes easier yet, it becomes $\frac{1}{2} \times \frac{4}{1}$ which equals $\frac{4}{2}$ or 2.

In sum, we make the divisor (or denominator) equal to one by multiplying it by its inverse. To keep the proportions equal we have to multiply the dividend (or numerator) also by the inverse of the divisor. Thus we can always turn a division of fractions problem into a simple multiplication problem — we just invert the denominator and multiply it by the numerator: $\frac{1}{2} \div \frac{1}{4} = \frac{1}{2} \times \frac{4}{1} = \frac{4}{2} = 2$.

Lets practice, first with some concrete manipulatives.

Divie Up

▶ **Concept:** Division of Fractions
(Invert & Multiply Algorithm)

▶ **Level:** *Concrete*

▶ **Materials:** Fraction Bars

▶ **Structure:** **Pairs Discuss**
Work in Pairs; Solve
Problems Together

Step 1

Lay out the problem with fraction bars.

$$\frac{1}{2} \div \frac{1}{4} =$$

Step 2

Add Fraction Pieces.
Add fraction pieces to the denominator (1/4) until it sums to one whole. Add the same number of fraction pieces to the numerator.

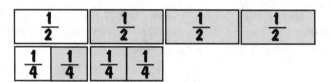

Step 3

Substitute one whole for the fraction pieces in the denominator.

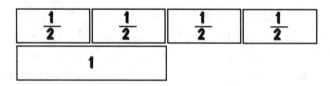

Step 4

Divide.
Count how many times the whole (denominator) will fit into the halves (numerator).

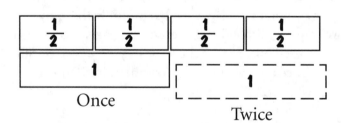

Once

Twice

Answer = 2

Note: If students are not clear about the meaning of dividing four halves by one, remind them as follows: When we ask, "What is seven divided by one," we are asking, "How many times will one whole fit into seven wholes?" Similarly, when we ask, "What is four halves divided by one," (4/2)/1, we are asking, "How many times will one whole fit into four halves." Dividing by one is finding how many wholes there are in a number.

Dividing Fractions

► **Concept:** Division of Fractions
(Invert & Multiply Algorithm)

► **Level:** *Connecting*

► **Materials:** Pencil, Paper

► **Structure:** **Think-Draw-Pair-Share**
Each individual builds each problem, then checks with her/his partner. Pairs check with the class.

Sample 1: $\frac{1}{2} \div \frac{1}{4}$

Step 1

Draw and label the problem.

$\frac{1}{2}$	$\frac{1}{2}$

$\frac{1}{4}$	$\frac{1}{4}$

Step 2

Draw More Fraction Pieces. Add enough pieces to make the denominator equal one, then add the same number of pieces to the numerator. Write it with numbers.

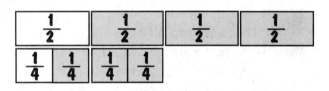

$$\frac{\frac{1}{2} \times \frac{4}{1}}{\frac{1}{4} \times \frac{4}{1}}$$

Step 3

Substitute one whole for the pieces in the denominator. Write the problem with numbers.

$\frac{1}{2}$	$\frac{1}{2}$	$\frac{1}{2}$	$\frac{1}{2}$

1

$$\frac{\frac{1}{2} \times \frac{4}{1}}{\frac{1}{4} \times \frac{4}{1}} = \frac{\frac{1}{2} \times \frac{4}{1}}{1}$$

Step 4

Divide. Count the number of times one will fit into the numberator. Write the problem with numbers.

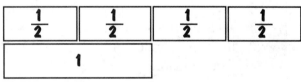

$$\frac{\frac{1}{2} \times \frac{4}{1}}{1} = \frac{4}{2} = 2$$

Note: Point out to students that Step 4 is what we do when we divide using the "Invert and Multiply" rule. After demonstrating several problems like the one on this page, you can have students complete a worksheet in which they alternate doing problems like those on page 88. The students can now write the full "Invert and Multiply" equation by each problem.

Short Cut Division

▶ **Concept:** Division of Fractions
(Invert & Multiply Algorithm)

▶ **Level:** *Symbolic*

▶ **Materials:** Pairs Check Worksheet, 1 per pair

▶ **Structure:** **Pairs Check**

Step 1

Listen to the problem: "One half divided by one fourth." Picture it three ways.

$$\frac{1}{4}\overline{\left)\frac{1}{2}\right.} \quad = \quad \frac{1}{2} \div \frac{1}{4} \quad = \quad \frac{\frac{1}{2}}{\frac{1}{4}}$$

Step 2

Multiply the Denominator $\left(\frac{1}{4}\right)$ by its reciprocal $\left(\frac{4}{1}\right)$, to make it equal one. Multiply the Numerator also by the reciprocal of the denominator, so the value of the fraction does not change.

$$\frac{\frac{1}{2} \times \frac{4}{1}}{\frac{1}{4} \times \frac{4}{1}}$$

Step 3

Multiply the fractions in the numerator and denominator, and reduce.

$$\frac{\frac{1}{2} \times \frac{4}{1}}{\frac{1}{4} \times \frac{4}{1}} \quad = \quad \frac{\frac{4}{2}}{\frac{4}{4}} \quad = \quad \frac{2}{1} \quad = \quad 2$$

Step 4

Short Cut Divison. Once students understand the process, have them just "Invert and Multiply," leaving out the denominator, which will always reduce to one.

$$\frac{1}{2} \div \frac{1}{4} \quad = \quad \frac{1}{2} \times \frac{4}{1} \quad = \quad \frac{4}{2} \quad = \quad 2$$

Dividing Fractions

WORKSHEET

Instructions: You must show all the steps. Reduce to lowest terms.

Pairs ✓

A _____ **B** _____

1. $\dfrac{1}{2} \div \dfrac{1}{6} =$	2. $\dfrac{3}{4} \div \dfrac{1}{8} =$	✓
3. $\dfrac{1}{3} \div \dfrac{1}{4} =$	4. $\dfrac{1}{4} \div \dfrac{1}{5} =$	✓
5. $\dfrac{5}{6} \div \dfrac{1}{3} =$	6. $\dfrac{1}{2} \div \dfrac{1}{3} =$	✓
7. $\dfrac{3}{4} \div \dfrac{1}{5} =$	8. $\dfrac{4}{5} \div \dfrac{1}{2} =$	✓
9. $\dfrac{1}{2} \div \dfrac{1}{4} =$	10. $\dfrac{3}{4} \div \dfrac{1}{2} =$	✓
11. $\dfrac{3}{4} \div \dfrac{1}{5} =$	12. $\dfrac{2}{3} \div \dfrac{1}{4} =$	✓
13. $\dfrac{2}{3} \div \dfrac{1}{3} =$	14. $\dfrac{3}{4} \div \dfrac{5}{8} =$	✓
15. $\dfrac{3}{5} \div \dfrac{1}{4} =$	16. $\dfrac{1}{4} \div \dfrac{1}{8} =$	✓
17. $\dfrac{3}{8} \div \dfrac{1}{4} =$	18. $\dfrac{5}{6} \div \dfrac{1}{4} =$	✓
19. $\dfrac{3}{4} \div \dfrac{1}{6} =$	20. $\dfrac{1}{3} \div \dfrac{2}{5} =$	✓

Resources & References

Baratta-Lorton, Robert. *Mathematics... A Way Of Thinking.* Menlo Park, CA: Addison-Wesley Publishing Company, 1977.

Bradford, John. *Everything's Coming Up Fractions with Cuisenaire Rods.* New Rochelle, NY: Cuisenaire Co.

Burns, Marilyn. *About Teaching Mathematics: A K-8 Resource.* White Plains, NY: Math Solutions Publications, 1992

Kagan, Spencer. *Cooperative Learning.* San Clemente, CA: Kagan Publishing, 1993.

Jenkins, Lee and McLean, Peggy. *Fraction Tiles.* Hayward, CA: Activity Resources Co.

National Council of Teachers of Mathematics. *Curriculum and Evaluation Standards for School Mathematics.* Reston, VA: NCTM, 1989.